*Praise for*

# ReBecoming: The Way of Opportunity

"'*ReBecoming*' is a really beautiful, inspirational story about a woman's quest for happiness. Never in my life have I found a character that I could relate as well to as I have with Diana Archer. There was so much in her story that I felt was written for myself and the healing that I need to do in my own life. I read it before I went to sleep at night and it definitely had an impact on my dreams. '*ReBecoming*' by J. R. Maxon made me feel like I was getting a gift from heaven."

— PAIGE LOVITT, READER VIEWS

"As I was reading this book, I kept getting the weirdest feeling: that the author knew me personally and had decided that he would write a book just for me. That is the kind of feeling you get when you read '*ReBecoming*'... sensitivity and insight. Through every sentence, imagery and emotion, there is a hidden message, an opposing point of view and a promise of something more... Yes, this book is absolutely about finding your spirituality, but it's also an explosion of joy at your life or the promise of what it can be! I really loved this book. It made me sad, happy and willing to work even more on my spiritual side."

— TINA AVON, REBECCA'S READS

"*ReBecoming* by J. R. Maxon is not only an intriguing and inspiring self-help book of fiction, but it also has a storyline that will hold the reader's interest from beginning to end. It takes a special kind of talent to accomplish such a task, and the author has shown such a talent. As someone who has done considerable counseling, I believe this book will truly show others 'the way of opportunity.' I believe all readers will agree that this book is life-changing; just reading it gives one hope for a future without fear. I hope you purchase a copy of this book for yourself and also for others that you care about. This is also a story of romance, threaded with breathtaking scenes of mystery, and danger. Within the pages of this 'must read' book, you will learn the secrets of becoming all that you can be."

— BETTIE CORBIN TUCKER, INDEPENDENT BOOK REVIEWERS

"Once I started reading this book, I found it difficult to put down. It is interesting, entertaining and funny. Most of all I found it to be a magical source for anyone trying to add some control to the destiny of their life. When I came to the conclusion, I knew I had just experienced something wonderful. I would recommend this book to anyone; especially those that want to make a difference in the future."
— NANCY EATON, BESTSELLERSWORLD.COM

"In the novel, *ReBecoming: The Way of Opportunity,* author J.R. Maxon delivers a spiritual and philosophical self-help guide in the form of a fictional story. With a goal of learning what it means to be happy, a number of themes are presented that include: an understanding of compassion, kindness, love, self-confidence, negative thoughts, physical appearance, relationships, finding courage, love, and self-love. The author successfully creates a protagonist that women can relate to. Readers may want to keep a pen and paper handy in order to note the many self-help techniques presented within the story. *ReBecoming: The Way of Opportunity* is highly recommended to readers who enjoy books about overcoming one's internal demons to gain an understanding of what it really means to be happy."
— TRACY ROBERTS, WRITE FIELD SERVICES

"Call it destiny…but something amazing happened to Diana. She decided to take control of her life…forced herself to go to the gym…got a trainer who understood that true health is more than a trim body, and he serves as a teacher, encouraging Diana to open up to all possibilities and find out who she truly wants to be."
— DR. TAMI BRADY, TCM REVIEWS

"I highly recommend *ReBecoming: The Way of Opportunity* to anyone seeking a better way to live, or a good thought-provoking read!"
— KELLY DAVIS, BOOKIDEAS.COM

"The book is especially good at suggesting how to improve attitudes and states of mind and the resultant outcomes of taking personal responsibility for one's life. We scored this very inspirational novel four hearts."
— BOB SPEAR, HEARTLAND REVIEWS

"When I finished reading this book, I just wanted to hug it."
— J. A. CAMPBELL, RETIRED VICE-PRESIDENT, ELF AQUITAINE

# ReBecoming

## The Way of Opportunity

### By

## J. R. Maxon

DASSANA

P R E S S
Insight from Reason

*ReBecoming* is a work of fiction. The characters are imaginary and of the author's creation. Any resemblance between these characters and actual persons living or dead is coincidental.

ReBecoming: The Way of Opportunity, the Rabbit in the Moon logo, and the Dassana Press bowl/fan logo are all trademarks of Dassana Press, LLC.

Copyright © 2009 by J. R. Maxon

Published by Dassana Press, LLC • P.O. Box-961 • Anna Maria, FL 34216

Cover Design by: 1106 Design • Interior Layout by: 1106 Design

ISBN: 978-0-9815201-5-5
$25.95

Printed in the U.S.A.
First Edition, January, 2009

PCN: 2008905565

**Publisher's Cataloging-in-Publication**
*(Provided by Quality Books, Inc.)*

Maxon, J. R. (Jonathan Rolfe)
   ReBecoming : the way of opportunity / by J.R. Maxon.
— 1st ed.
   p. cm.
   LCCN 2008905565
   ISBN-13: 978-0-9815201-5-5
   ISBN-10: 0-9815201-5-4

   1. Life change events—Fiction. 2. Self-actualization (Psychology)—Fiction. 3. Mind and body—Fiction. 4. Psychological fiction, American. I. Title.

PS3613.A888R43 2009       813'.6
                QBI08-600307

# Chapters

*Lean back, and hold onto nothing!*

*Someone* once told me events are cowards—always running in packs. In the year I turned thirty-three, a series of unsettling events unexpectedly came to see me. At first they were only mildly troubling, but when they appeared more frequently, I had to take notice. Then life became strange and very serious.

Andrea and I have looked back and debated many times about exactly what they meant. We've disagreed on whether it was luck or misfortune, and about how it all began. But I think it was fate, and I know it started early one Friday evening on a beach by the dark salty waters of Tampa Bay.

# Chapter One: Choice Secrets

*"All of life is but a parade of choices."*

"**Someday**," I whispered, bathing in sunset colors, lightning in my heart, thunder in my head. Below, two watched from the beach as I reached out a cloudy hand...

"Diana, please. Let's go! It's scary out here!"

In a flash, my thunderhead vision ended and I slammed back into my heavy flesh.

Overhead, shore birds streamed across the bay toward Mullet Key as the evening band of storms marched our way—flickering, growing, changing, and unstoppable.

Then as the twilight full moon emerged from behind a towering grey pillar and the waters between us gleamed with her bright reflection, I imagined the silver sparkle pointed directly at me. I took a deep breath, and made a silent wish.

I felt a tug on my sleeve.

"Can we leave now?" Andrea begged, impatient, adding an urgent, "I don't want to get wet! My hair will frizz."

"In a minute," I said. "There's a blue moon tonight." And I pointed to it.

With a petulant twist of her sandals in the shells, her narrowed eyes glanced upward. "It's not blue to me."

"Maybe a bit in its halo," I said as she fidgeted.

But perhaps talking would calm her so I asked, "What do you see when you look at the moon?"

"Just the moon."

"You don't see patterns?"

"Well, everyone else sees a *man,* I suppose, but I see a scorpion tail over its head—ready to strike!"

Never having seen a scorpion in the moon, I thought for a second and then told her a story.

"A scorpion once asked a frog for a ride across a stream. The kind frog hesitated because if the scorpion stung him during the swim, he would drown. The scorpion promised not to do this, but mid-way across the water the frog felt the sharp stab of the scorpion's stinger. As he sank, the frog cried out, 'Why did you do that? Now we're both lost!' To this the scorpion answered, 'I had to. I couldn't do otherwise. It's my nature.'"

A silent moment followed.

"It's my nature," Andrea repeated. "I don't get it. Why do you keep telling me these things, especially tonight?"

"I don't know," I replied. But I did know a little. I knew it wasn't my nature to be afraid or unkind and I knew I had to look to the future and to the good.

"If you don't know, then quit." Her silk skirt flapped as her words faded into a gust of wind.

I stopped speaking, but couldn't stop thinking, and I felt *something.* Maybe your senses can tell you when change is coming if you slow down long enough to listen.

"And when it comes this time," I quietly vowed, "I'm going to recognize and appreciate it."

Then, resolved, as the first drops fell, I said louder, "Okay. Let's go in."

Andrea clapped, elated.

✴

A big, one-legged pirate with a black eye patch stood guard, and as we crossed the broad, lantern-lit porch, he grinned. A cutlass in a tasseled scabbard and a golden key dangled from his wide belt as he doffed his feathered Jolly Roger hat and opened the door.

"Welcome ladies," his baritone bellowed.

I smiled, no curtseys for me, and as Andrea hesitated, looking at the wooden treasure chest on the porch next to the heavy oak doors, I said, "Clean your plate, then we'll see." Maybe she recalled our last visit when after a friendly pirate squeeze she'd gleefully pulled a cloud-covered zeppelin toy from the chest's depths.

Inside, the hostess scribbled my name on a list and pointed to the bar beyond a bubbling salt-water aquarium. A ship's bell would ring when our table was ready. We knew the stated twenty-minute wait would be an hour or more, but on that Friday night, dateless, there was no hurry.

We ventured forward and were transported onto a galleon. Flickering lights hung from the thick-beamed ceiling and cast swaying rays onto shiny pine paneling and a polished wooden floor. It was wonderfully cool and dim and there was a tang of hope in the air.

We crossed the crowded room to the only two empty stools at the bar and as I slid onto mine, a myriad of silver dollars winked up at me like minnows swimming just below the bar's clear surface.

Andrea, true to form, smiled seductively at the barskipper and we ordered.

Spot-lit paintings of wave-tossed ships under full sail filled the walls beyond Andrea's head. On a shelf sat a large pink conch with a right-handed turn and on the wall beside it a length of thick white rope was woven into an endless knot. My eyes followed the patterns around and around.

But to me the most intriguing feature of all was the wooden prow of a ship projecting from the wall above the center of the bar. Its thinly clad figurehead smiled down at me as if she were having difficulty keeping a secret. That evening I was seated beneath her and as I tilted my head I could just make out the ship's name in the low light and flaking gilt paint. It was: *The Willing Mind*.

My musing was interrupted. Our drinks had arrived.

As I reached into my purse a voice to my right said, "Thank you. On my bill, please."

The barskipper nodded and walked away and my eyes arrived on my neighbor.

They saw a well-dressed gentleman whose smiling face had developed what my grandmother would have called character. Above a strong jaw and a closely trimmed salt and pepper beard, with more salt than pepper, his wide-set eyes were full of life. The kind of eyes that say, "Someone is home." They were greenish-gray and flecked with white, and as I gazed into them my mind traveled out over the ocean. I saw tides and sky; I saw quiet and depth. My initial impulse was to refuse, but as I looked into his face, only kindness and generosity were displayed. Eager intentions were absent.

"Thank you," I said, and then returned to Andrea.

And although I'd only briefly ignored her, the two business men to Andrea's left had finished their discussion and refocused their attention. She was beaming and I was forgotten.

"What brings you to this fine dining establishment on this auspicious evening?" the gentleman asked.

I swiveled back to him.

"My name is Stefan," he said offering me his hand.

"Pleased to meet you. I'm Diana and this is Andrea." She didn't notice. "I'm taking her to dinner. She's been through a lot lately and needs to be treated special." I sympathetically patted her arm.

"You're a compassionate person, Diana," he said, "and she's fortunate to have such a caring friend."

"Thanks. My grandmother always taught me to be kind and I try to remember her words."

"Wonderful," Stefan said. "Because no matter what happens, kindness and good manners are always appropriate."

"So, what brings you here this evening?" I asked in return.

"I'm meeting two good friends for dinner," he said, glancing around and reflecting, "And I've made such pleasant memories in this old Inn."

"So have I. My mother used to bring me here for birthdays." Then comfortable so far I decided to be bold. He was looking into my eyes again and something compelled me. "If you don't mind my asking, what do you do for a living?" I always try to guess, but with him I hadn't any idea.

"I'm a pilot and a navigator. And you?"

I hadn't expected such a brief answer as most men would have expounded profusely so I swallowed quickly and replied, "I work for a software company on the north side of Tampa." I too was brief because the trick was not to reveal yourself, but also not to lie.

"How do you like your job, Diana?"

"It used to be better," I answered. "You know what I mean." But no one could understand.

"Yes, unfortunately I do. But that's when your other life choices make up for work. Right?"

"I guess. But everyday is too busy for me to have much choice." My words were peppered with frustration and I broke my own rule as personal feelings leaked out.

"My new friend I must disagree with you," Stefan said with a gentle shake of his head. "We choose anew each moment and the choices we make determine who we are and how happy we will be.

And by making the same choices over and over, our lives appear to have continuity. But if with time our choices change, then we change."

"Yes, but sometimes life just happens. Then you don't get to choose your choices."

"Oh, but you do," he said, leaning closer to me and poking his finger on the bar. "How did you come to be here tonight? Your choices played out through time. You made specific decisions, some with instinct and some with thought. And even if you chose the one marked, 'None of the above,' that also was a choice. All of life is but a parade of choices."

"Yes," I said, as I tried not to get involved, "but to answer your question, I don't know how I got to this point. It did just happen. In fact it happened so fast I wonder about it." I shook my head. He seemed sincere and he probably thought informative, but he wasn't right. He hadn't lived my life.

"So what about Andrea?" I asked. "Her stepfather has left her mother again and she's very upset. She's suffering. How could she avoid that?"

"You're correct. She has no say in her loved one's matters. Where her decision lies is in how she accepts it. Her suffering is a choice."

"A choice? Her suffering is not a choice! What if you get hurt? Then you suffer!" I was on the verge of being rude.

"Ah," he said. "If by hurt you mean physical pain, then you've added a new dimension. Physical pain may become inevitable, but mental anxiety is always an option. Pain and suffering are different things."

"Well, you'll have to explain that to Andrea!" I said, not wanting to get angry.

"I'll do that. And since I've piqued your interest, let me offer you both an invitation. As I said, I'm waiting for two friends, ones

I'm sure you would enjoy meeting. So please, will you and Andrea join us for dinner? It would be my pleasure."

"Fine," was on my tongue when slurry voices returned me to the reality of my friend. The men next to her were heated. Then one of them stroked her bare leg and I heard him ask if she wore panties and could he please see.

Her curt refusal upset him. "No" was not in his mind.

Andrea excused herself, but as she slid off her stool the man rubbed her bottom and then tried to lift the hem of her short white skirt. With a killer look she huffed away and after a few moments he followed.

I should have gone with her, but I assumed she'd be safe. I sipped at my wine. And then, "You've been smiling the whole time we've been talking," I said to Stefan with some tartness. "You must have a wonderful life. You're so lucky."

"Hmm," he said, stroking his whiskers with his fingertips. "Luck is a lot like the tide, Diana. It always goes out, turns, and comes back in again—for everyone. But it also depends on a person's expectations. You can't be a lazy fisherman because, as in life, timing is everything. And yes, I smile because I'm happy and I'm happy because I choose to be."

"You *choose* to be happy?"

He took a breath to answer and—my phone rang. It was Andrea, frantic, calling from the parking lot and demanding we leave immediately.

As I jumped off my stool Stefan placed his hand on mine and said, "Remember, Diana, serenity is not freedom from the storm, but calm within the storm." He took a card from his jacket and stuck it into my purse. I didn't look at it. I hurried away and the memory of his conversation faded as the urgency of Andrea grew. Then racing past the surprised pirate I entered the thick night air.

As we sped away, Andrea told me the man had followed her to the restroom and waited outside. When she came out, and ducked back in, he'd pounded on the door and called her unpleasant names. Afraid, she'd kicked open the window, slithered through it, and ruined her fresh pedicure as she ran to the car.

What she could not understand, she told me, was why these things happened to *her* whenever we went out, especially since it was *my* treat. She was amusing to watch when I told her we'd been invited to join a group of male friends for dinner—*their* treat. She slapped her forehead and slid down in her seat. A curse escaped her lips.

The following Wednesday we met for lunch. Andrea and I worked in the same part of town and we got together every few days when our bosses were out of town or at a favorite club. That day she'd told her manager she needed to have her eye checked, and when she limped over to sit she told me to check it. I did and although it was in its proper place, it was full of mad.

"What happened to you?" I asked.

In addition to everything with her parents, she explained, Andrea's romantic pairing had ended that past weekend, roughly. On Sunday morning her boyfriend had gone out to get donuts, beer, and a paper to check the games. As he hurried back with his mouth full of gooey treats and his mind full of waterbed, he took a curve too fast and her new sports car rolled over eagerly rubbing its sides and top.

At home she'd been longing for breakfast pastries when he arrived unhurt, but with the police. His grapey, bewildered expression and flimsy excuse aroused her fury. Then after the police left he complained of being tense and would she please help with a massage and sex. She'd gotten so mad she'd burst a blood vessel in her left eye and peering through its bleary curtain she told me she'd given up on men. Again.

"I should have *known* he was trouble," she said. "The day before, one of his running shoes came off and I tripped and twisted my ankle. If I can't run I'll get pudgy and my clothes won't fit." She eyed me.

I wanted to say some of them barely fit anyway, but instead I asked, "What now, kick boxing class again?"

"No, I've got a better idea."

I almost said, "I don't want to hear it!" I remembered the nude yoga class. "Your body can breathe!" she'd gasped when trying to get me to attend. I'd declined then and was prepared to decline any new proposal.

"We're joining the Four Palms Fitness Club! I saw a giant full-color ad in the Sunday paper, called, and signed us up for a two-week free membership. We're going next Monday night!"

Cheese-coated peas impacted the backs of my front teeth. "What?" I gurgled as peas swirled into my stomach.

"You already signed us up? Why would I want to go to a gym with sweaty people?" It had to be her eye—she couldn't see straight.

"That's just like you," she said, gesturing at my crossed arms. "You hear about something new and right away it's, 'No.' This will be a lot of fun. And think about all the men. They'll be in great shape."

"Didn't you just say you'd sworn off men?"

"I meant men for *you*. Not for me. And after all I've been through, the very *least* you can do is come with me the first time. Anyway, you're going to love it and one day you'll thank me."

"What if I have to work late?"

"No way! I'll call your boss and tell him you have to leave early because you have a hot date." She smiled smugly. She knew I had problems at work, she just didn't know what they were.

"No, don't do that," I said, defeated. "I'll pick you up."

Later I saw she'd been clever. Football season was over and lots of men would be free on Monday nights. And what could be better than going to the gym to ogle women?

Then gym Monday arrived and I had second thoughts.

When I'd turned off the ignition, Andrea grinned with victory, but then saw the battle wasn't over. My hands thumped the steering wheel.

"You're coming in *with* me! I am not going in there by myself!" she said as she grabbed at my keys and missed.

"Okay! Okay!"

"At last! Grab your bag and come on!"

I had to smile at my friend Andrea. We had known each other a long time: all the way through high school and college, community college for her and USF for me, and we'd stayed close ever since. She'd even lived with me for a while after her divorce.

So I knew Andrea wasn't always overly dramatic, but I also knew that sometimes she felt she wasn't being heard. Her solution was to emphasize certain words and to use hand gestures to punctuate her speech. I'd never quite been able to figure out which words got the emphasis and which got the gestures, but they were a part of what made Andrea my friend and except for her unceasing problems with men, she was what my grandmother would have called "a good egg."

Discussion ended, we got out and walked to the door. As I grasped its metal handle, Andrea whispered, "Don't forget it's *free*."

Once inside, I nervously surveyed the lobby looking for escape paths while Andrea talked to a girl at the desk. When she finished, we sat on a couch.

"Hi! I'm Jim Campbell, your personal fitness coordinator. Welcome!" A tall blond man wearing khaki shorts and a maroon, form-fitting shirt emblazoned with four bright red palm trees, both on the front and back, had joined us. He looked fit and a little younger than us.

He smiled and shook our hands, but as I looked into his blue eyes I knew in an instant I was ahead on points. Usually when I went places with Andrea she got all the attention, but this man's focus was on me and it felt good.

His eyes only briefly left mine as he said, "I'll give you a tour after you fill out this form." Then he fumbled the papers as he was handing them to us. Embarrassed, he rapidly scooped them up. Andrea frowned.

We filled in the questionnaires. On the line labeled "Sex," Andrea wrote "not in here." On my form I invented an address and phone number and lied about my weight.

As Andrea finished I noticed Four Palms smelled like a new car—plastic, rubber, and metal. I'd expected a locker room aroma of sweaty base notes capped with a bouquet of testosterone. But the air was clean and I found my idea to come here only once losing strength. The people looked normal and some looked a lot better than normal.

"Thanks!" Jim collected our forms. "Now it's time for your tour."

"Wow!" was all Andrea said when we stepped around the desk and into the main gym area. The place was huge, brightly lit, and intimidating.

"You'll be happy here," Jim said. "We have the very best of everything." He smiled at *me*.

When Andrea saw this she said crisply, "I want to bike."

"Wait. Let's take our tour first," Jim said as he started to walk away.

"I have loads of gym experience," Andrea stated. She didn't. "I don't need a tour. You two can go on."

I quickly decided I wasn't going alone on a gym tour with a strange personal trainer salesman guy.

"Don't you want to put your bags in lockers first?" Jim asked.

"No. We'll keep them with us," Andrea replied in a voice that said, "No further discussion allowed."

"Okay...suit yourselves." His sails flapped and I felt a little sorry for him. "I'll be in the trainer area. Wave if you want anything."

"We will." I wanted to smile at him, but Andrea scowled.

"Come on," she said and led the way.

The bicycles were on a raised platform. Behind them, in addition to treadmills, were other strange pieces of exercise equipment. The men and women using them looked hot.

We walked up the four steps and mounted the bikes. This was a good vantage point. If we were hunters we'd have the high ground. I started to pedal because I didn't want to look conspicuous which wasn't difficult since I wore a baggy blue tee shirt and loose shorts.

But Andrea had dressed to thrill. With her tight tank top, long straight hair in a ponytail, and heavy makeup, she'd attract any male bees within range. And I'd smelled fragrance in the car so I knew her resolution was a bust.

The biking was easy. Later I'd learn you had to turn them on and set the controls before it did any good. But for a while tonight we laughed, talked about girl stuff, and complained about everything.

Then after barely half an hour, things changed. Killer bees took note of the new flowers and began to buzz. Gradually they flew closer and closer, stingers ready. At first, Andrea tried to pretend they weren't there, but as they hummed around she shot them hot little glances.

"How do you like that one?" Andrea asked as she pointed with her head. "He's cute!"

"No. He's not. He's got funny teeth, probably fake. Pay attention or you'll fall off." To me, he also seemed preoccupied with himself. And because she'd dragged me along I wanted to talk to her and not to some big-stinger bee. But he lit.

Their snickering conversation was the usual superficial search for similarities so they'd have an excuse to see each other again. But I saw her look away once to watch one of the personal trainers slowly walk by.

I watched him too, and with interest. As he passed he glanced up and a fiery spark touched the base of my spine. Then the heated ember rose until it popped somewhere behind my heart. He didn't stop.

"That trainer looks good! He has nice legs," Andrea was commenting. I was biking. "Go for it!"

"What? Go where?"

"I've never seen you that way," she said as she smiled at the trainer's retreating rear.

"Give me a break! He's probably married or something. Besides we came here to exercise, not to chase men. Or have you forgotten?"

What she'd forgotten was that she already had a buzzing bee ready to sting. Now I saw he'd gone to the snack bar in the front of the gym and was on his way back with two and only two protein drinks. With a grin he handed one to Andrea while he slurped on the other.

His toothy smiles at me were wasted, but Andrea was enchanted by his wit. She laughed and laughed at his semi-whispered crude gym humor. But after some minutes of their giggles I decided I'd had enough.

"Tomorrow's a busy day, Andrea. Let's go home." I left out my disappointment.

Sensing a possible failure to secure the honey, her new friend whispered and then rushed to the front desk. His winged feet singed the rubber matting.

"Larry will be right back. Just hold on." She wasn't happy to leave.

"Sure. I'll meet you by the door." I dismounted and went to the stairs. But as I descended I turned to see what Andrea was doing and...my foot missed the second step.

In movies, important scenes are slowed so the audience can see every detail. With my mind as audience, this happened to me. As my left foot stumbled, my right foot tried to grab the edge of the step. This pushed me out and as gravity took hold, down. My bag went flying as my arms pin wheeled and my mouth and eyes became O's. I envisioned a painful, rubbery impact with the floor.

It never happened. A maroon shirt with palms appeared and I collided with it. Hard! It barely moved as I slid down its back and came to rest on the bottom step. After a shrug, the back turned to a front and I looked up into sparkling hazel eyes. It was the trainer who'd walked by!

"Please stay calm," he said. "You need to rest after a fall to resettle your body and mind. Others can step around you."

"Okay," I said, breathless, and not entirely from the tumble.

I heard steps behind me and Andrea patted me on the head. "I can't take you anywhere, Diana. I thought you'd be safe in here and now look at this. You'll do *anything* to get a man's attention." She gestured.

Embarrassed, I started to rise, but the trainer said, "No, stay seated for a moment longer. I want to be sure you're all right."

"Well, aren't you *trying* to be a gentleman tonight," Andrea teased and I saw her shift gears. "But if you *were* a gentleman, you'd have caught her in your arms."

"While romantic," the trainer replied, ignoring Andrea's batting eyes, "her momentum would have propelled us both onto the floor. This way I was braced and she could fall no farther." He looked at her for a reply.

She had none because Larry had buzzed back with an all-important pen borrowed from the desk. And while he grinned and grunted he wrote her vital numerals on his muscled forearm, which looked like it'd been shaved. Then he raised the arm to his lips and in a tacky gesture, he kissed her digits. This was too much even for Andrea, who said, "Call me." He flapped off happily, bee arms snaking, and I hoped he'd soon forget and sweat the numbers away.

"You can stand up now." The trainer had been watching me during the number drama and now offered his hand.

As I grasped it, ecstatic energy raced up my arm. For a moment I was somewhere else. I saw a pond with lavender flowers growing tall out of pale green water. And as he helped me to rise, the view faded. He let go and handed me my bag.

"Thank you. We have to leave," I said as my feet staggered toward the door.

"I understand. Please come and see…" the trainer's voice trailed off as we walked away. I didn't look back.

As I drove her home Andrea put her hand on my shoulder, "If you don't want him, I do. You can have the first shot, but if you miss, I want mine. We've been friends a long time, you and I, but men are men and if a friend lets one go, he becomes fair game."

I nodded, silent. My vision: he and I strolling, holding each other, beside the pool of beautiful flowers.

# Chapter Two: Investment in a Garden

*"You will grow so far beyond yourself it will
be like comparing a shrub to an oak."*

*Inside* my mind a battle raged. One voice yelled, "Go back! You want to see him!" Another cried, "No! Don't be too eager! He'll have the advantage!" But the worst voice of all whispered, "What do you think he'll see in *you*? You're out of shape and you're not desirable. Stay home. Save yourself the heartache." It was impossible to think clearly about anything after this last voice had murmured its vicious, biting words.

But my time of return was delayed. Late office meetings filled the rest of the week and every night before I went to sleep I'd tell myself that I would go back to Four Palms and that I'd go…tomorrow. But piles of pages built into mountains and when the weekend arrived I thought the gym would be too crowded so I didn't go then either.

When Monday evening came again I ignored my misgivings and convinced myself I was eager to bike. I shoved an oversized tee shirt and shorts into my bag and rehearsed responses in anticipation to questions *he* might ask.

Traffic was heavy, stop and go. I was capable of numerous activities while driving, but when I reached down to retrieve my breath spray I noticed a second too late the bus ahead of me had stopped. I slammed on my brakes and avoided an impact, but relief was fleeting. Behind me, a rusty white pickup truck missing part of its front bumper couldn't stop. The bang from the impact was deafening. My head slammed into the headrest, rebounded into the steering wheel, and bounced off the side window. Things became blurry.

I woke up strapped to a gurney. My sides and head hurt and lights were bright rings. As the burly EMT's rolled me into the ambulance I smelled and heard more than saw a beer-soaked, gnarly man belching and blaming while his handcuffed buddy danced a jig. Then it was a siren-screaming ride to the hospital.

One fantasy I'd never imagined was a fast run through city streets while helplessly strapped down and surrounded by big, peppermint-scented men. But the painful sloshing as we raced and cornered restrained any thoughts of pleasure.

The hospital stay mended my body, but it weakened my spirit and when Andrea came to visit she leaned over and whispered that the trainer had asked about me. Upset, I made her swear she would absolutely under no circumstances reveal my pathetic state. She agreed, but late one night, hazy with medication, I thought I saw his face hovering over my bed. My eyelids were heavy and after they reopened, he was gone.

Released from the hospital, I spent the next week in recovery at home. The doctor's orders required a dim apartment, limited computer, television, and reading, and no gyrating around. As the trainer had said, I was to stay calm. But it had been a long time since I'd had to sit alone quietly, even for a few minutes.

At first it was relaxing as I reflected on friends, relatives, and the past. But happy thoughts soon turned stormy when I thought about the present and then my future. And after a few days I was a crazy woman and had discovered a terrible fact. I had no control over my mind. Untamed beasts roared inside my head.

Strong feelings of always being trapped and disappointed arose as I realized I would never get what I wanted and needed. It would forever elude me. I would never be satisfied. And each hurried day kept me that way.

The accident and the enforced peace had ripped open my complacency. Urgency laced with fear compelled me to look at my life unmasked. The truth glared at me from between busyness curtains. My life was running away and there was little I could do to slow it down.

Then gradually and deliberately my thoughts changed and a new resolve formed. I was going to return my life to one of happiness and love. I was going to become desirable, find someone to love me, and then I would be happy. I would start right away and nothing could dissuade me from my goal now that I saw clearly. I went to sleep actually looking forward to returning to work the next day.

"Couldn't you get back any sooner?" Mr. Dawl, my boss, grumbled as I stepped off the elevator. His face was a sour prune and I wasn't surprised that he'd been waiting for me. "We don't pay you to get hurt," he added.

Later that morning he came by my office to remind me that if I shouldered my burden and did what was right, everything would be fine for me. What he meant was that if I worked overtime he wouldn't get into trouble with his boss and he would still get his bonus. That was important because Mr. Dawl was buying his daughter a new Lexus convertible.

The next two weeks were packed with extra work and my new resolve, including the gym plan, was nearly forgotten. But then at the end of a long grueling day coupled with someone's flat tire which had backed traffic up into the twilight zone, I arrived home to find a message from Andrea. We hadn't spoken for a while and she came right to the point.

Everything was going great in her life. She was in better shape and hoped I would get my act together soon. And oh, there was one other thing. Larry was having a problem with *commitment*, I could hear the emphasis and see the gestures, and he might be leaving. So in regards to the trainer from the gym, he's unattached. And by the way if I wasn't interested in him to please tell her. She ended by saying he kept asking if I was well and when was I coming in.

As I listened I detected guilt. From this I surmised she'd told everyone about my accident.

A little annoyed, I called and left my own message that said, "Yes, I'd been out of it, but that was over." And, "Yes, he was mine."

I felt better afterwards, but also a little strange in claiming an unknown man for my own.

Over the following weekend I tried to get into the exercise spirit by using the gadget I'd gotten from a late-night infomercial, but I couldn't squeeze out any motivation. I knew Andrea had progressed from the free trial to a full membership so I needed to get busy fast.

On Monday I made my second attempt to begin and as I trekked to the front door of the Four Palms Fitness Club I watched others aimed at the same cheery portal. Most walked with a spring in their step and since it was after 6 p.m., I wondered if they'd gone to work that day. Maybe it was a holiday my company didn't observe because if they'd been exhausted like me, they would have been dragging not bouncing.

After a brief wait, the front desk girl looked at me with amused interest as she took my expired card and I was referred to Jim.

"Hi! Remember me?" His face glowed in the overhead glare and he was helpful and excited. At last he got his chance and would not be dissuaded from explaining all about the equipment and facilities: basketball court, aerobics room, heated pool, and a co-ed spa for relaxing and meeting. He winked as he mentioned the spa. There were wet and dry saunas, and lots and lots of the finest, shiniest, and most up-to-date exercise equipment.

In the past I'd watched men and women on television who were working out. They were shapely, smiling, and I'd concluded that they must be happy.

"Have you decided on the level of membership you'd like?" Jim asked. "From the looks of you the full membership package is what I recommend. And you can pay by check or charge."

"What do you mean 'from the looks of me'?" After my accident I was sensitive to people's "looks."

"I didn't mean it that way, Diana," he backpedaled fast. "I only meant you look ready for a change. You want to become a new you, a better you, don't you? Not that you're so bad now, but we can all improve can't we?" At first he looked unsure, and then this changed to a smile. I had to laugh. He was either genuine or very well rehearsed. I chose genuine.

"Is this membership a good value?" In the past I'd found my promiscuous credit cards could not be relied on for guidance.

"If you use your membership you're getting a bargain, but if we never see you again, what you've spent you've wasted."

My grandmother always said, "A penny wasted is truly a penny wasted." So if I joined I'd have to use my membership or feel guilty. I decided it would be an investment—an investment in me.

"Okay, I'll join," I said.

"Great. Now how about personal training sessions to give you a good start? We have the most qualified personal trainers available. Each one is certified," he glanced around and added in a low voice, "like the best brands of beef."

I laughed. "I guess I could use help getting started. Do I get to pick the trainer or does the gym choose for me? I've only been here once."

"I've got the perfect one," he said. "His name is Jon and he's not here tonight, but you can meet him on Wednesday."

"Fine. Tell me about him."

"Well…here's a vitamin coupon. Your new membership gives you a discount in our shop. Plus we've got a new line of workout clothes."

"That's good. Now about the trainer. Would I know him if I saw him?" I'd noticed a display of photos on the wall coming in.

His hands tapped on the desk. "Yes," he said slowly. Then faster, "You nearly knocked him down." And after a moment of concentration he became bold, "The man who wants to be your trainer has been waiting for you. Jon got your name from Andrea and asked us to assign him if you wanted personal training, but we were not to pressure you."

"And that's the whole story?"

"Yes, that's it. But you won't tell him will you? I value his friendship."

"Your secret's safe." But my gossipy friend Andrea wasn't.

Then as he looked on expectantly I said, "All right. I've decided. Sign me up for the full membership and the personal training package too."

"Right away. And you aren't making a mistake." He typed quickly. "Plus! The snack bar makes great drinks. Have you tried a protein shake?"

"I've seen them, but I've never had one."

"Then let's finish this paperwork and I'll treat you."

I pretended not to hear his last remark and waited for an opening to ask again about the trainer who had waited for me.

As I signed the contracts, Jim added, "Your life will now change and you will grow so far beyond yourself it will be like comparing a shrub to an oak."

But before I could ask him to explain, the club manager came over to welcome me and when I turned back to Jim, he'd moved to a different desk and was talking to another client. He looked up at me and winked again.

I left the sales booth and as I walked out onto the main gym floor still holding the pen I'd used to sign, I felt the beginning twinges of buyer's remorse.

Then as I looked up, the mighty lights from ten thousand suns beamed down on me from the distant ceiling. The impact of their brightness was so physical that I closed my eyes and a strange scene unfolded.

Naïve and unsuspecting, I slowly descended a dim, stone stairway, each narrow granite tread deeply worn in its center. At the bottom, a pitted metal door with rusty bolt-heads swung wide with crying echoes of hysteria that ran up and down the stairs behind me as I entered a dark-ish, dungeon-ish place. It was an ancient workout chamber.

Sights bordered on the ragged edge of anything I could have imagined.

Bare bulbs hung from dirty cords and swayed in the heavy air while waves of smelly moisture and sere mustiness caressed me as I stared into a long room bathed in a sickly glare reminiscent of badly stained teeth.

Shocked, I grabbed at the walls for balance and as I did, pieces of peeling paint pulled away to reveal syrupy drops of condensed sweat. Then as dollops dripped from the curling edges, my steamy eyes pictured the globules as dirty pearls.

Following one as it fell I saw it hurry into a rusty, hair-coated drain set into dirty white tiles. Each filthy square was shattered into a pattern of spider-webbed cracks and, in an evil parody of snowflakes, each had its own unique design.

As I probed deeper into the room, other troubling aspects seeped into my consciousness. In the wavering light I saw that heavy torture had caused cottony blossoms to erupt from cracks in black-coated, metal machines. These sinister implements, each with its own bad intentions, allowed brutish men and women to join with them in a heated union of grunting and clanking that climaxed in hot satisfaction. This animated intercourse with machine after machine in frenzied motion was mirrored by their dark shadows erotically entwined on the walls.

My eyes then tried to focus on the shimmering reflections on the skins of those beings. But the hazy scenes were difficult to discern as their glistening bodies executed rituals using long metal bars and thick iron plates to a rhythm of heavy thuds. And as my bones vibrated, I knew I must run away now or never, ever, leave.

But as I turned to escape, a hulk blocked my way.

"Here to work it out, Diana?" Words drooled from watery lips. He stepped close to me, his body glowed with heat. His every muscle was hard; his skin stretched tight. My bottom bumped the wall and oily liquid oozed down my bare legs.

"I don't know what to do," I squeaked, backing away as I saw his toes, attached to leg-like trunks, rooting into the dirty-cracked tiles.

"I can show you how to get what you want," mouthed the hulk. His toothy stubs were red-tipped, mossy brown daggers.

"I only want to be happy and content in my own skin, in my own body, no matter what it looks like!" I cried. "That's all!" Falling into a momentary quiet my words raced to the far end of the room and then back to my ears.

For a second the hulk looked like he'd eaten raw liver bathed in hot sauce. Then a putrid roar of laughter laced with bits of steamed food erupted from his bottomless throat. Everyone turned to look, each adding his or her own raucous caw. Some stuck out their arms, thumbs turned downward.

"Happy? Content?" he yelled, his bulging eyes inches from mine. "You're doomed to a life of discontent and dis-ease. And," his chewed, dirty-nailed finger stopped a hair from my nose, "you're doomed to exist, not to live, only to exist. There's no way out, no exit. So abandon any hope because to resist your fate is futile." A fierce glare. Then flinging sweat he stomped away.

Choking on my despair-bathed heart, I fled up the stairs from this horrific scene as I heard the metal door behind me scream shut with a doomed finality. Breathless, I burst forth into the welcoming sunshine and, oh…the sweetness of the air!

As I lay on my back among grass and flowers, inexpressible joy washed over me. I was so blessed to have escaped a fate inflicted only on the willing.

I swayed and took a step back.

A hand gently grasped my shoulder. "Don't leave yet, please," said a familiar voice. "I'd like to talk with you and perhaps show you around."

"I'm not leaving. I...the lights are brighter than I remember." I looked at the floor as the image of the nasty tiles faded.

"The ceiling is so high management thought we needed stronger lights. Now the shadows cast shadows." The voice moved around to the front.

It was him! It was the trainer I'd smashed! He looked fine tonight, but before I could say anything, Jim came over. He literally ran.

"I thought..." Jim began, and then hesitated.

"...that I wasn't coming back," the trainer finished. "I saw her in the parking lot and decided to see how she was doing after her accident."

"Hello, Diana. I'm Jon," he said.

We shook hands.

"How are you feeling? Are you recovered?"

Andrea...she's toast...she's burnt toast, I thought, along with other vile things. She couldn't keep it shut. She owed me big time and I imitated one of her gestures. And from the way the two of them looked at me and then at each other, they probably thought I still wasn't well.

"I feel tight and sore in spots, but otherwise I'm fine." I didn't notice my hurts unless I thought about them.

"She signed up for personal training with you," Jim blurted out.

Maybe he got points for being the first to tell. My co-workers gained their points by hurrying to spread bad news.

"You didn't press her did you?" my new trainer asked, favoring Jim with a look that would have withered the freshest lilies.

"No. There was no pressure."

"I made the decision myself," I said.

Jim and Jon exchanged another glance and I sensed something under the surface.

"Take her on a tour," Jim said, being helpful.

"In a moment. She needs to quiet down first. But there might be other clients who require your expertise, so we'll see you later."

"Ah…right. I see them." There weren't any clients. "Stop by if you need anything. And that's his pen." Jim pointed to my hand.

"She can keep it. She might need it one day."

Then as Jim left, Jon said with a sweep of his hand, "Are you ready for your grand tour?"

"Yes, sir!" I saluted and then quickly thought, where did that come from?

Under the blazing lights and accompanied by a guide, my experience was fresh and I surprised myself by noticing that even after knowing him for only minutes, I was becoming comfortable with his smile.

As we walked together we entered a garden of shining chrome. Trails appeared and soon I could see a pattern to the labyrinth. Uncountable pieces of padded exercise equipment in every shape and size crouched in long rows and in the distance they converged like railroad tracks.

Some machines stood tall with long silver branches. Others were squat and their limbs rose and fell in time with the jungle rhythms blasting from speakers dangling from the ceiling like strange electronic fruit. Potted silk plants formed small green islands and bits of color resolved into people who looked like tropical birds flying tree-to-tree, pausing here and there to chatter.

To my right was the platform where Andrea and I had begun this journey. Behind the bicycles I saw men and women exercising on machines composed of rising stairs. Some were stepping slowly while others were jogging, but all were ascending and never reaching the top. Wall mirrors reflected their strained expressions and dark-stained shirt backs. I looked away. It reminded me of work.

"Impressive isn't it, Diana?"

For the first time I noticed Jon was more attentive than most men. He listened with what he would later term one-pointedness, before he replied. He never interrupted my mouth or my mind and even more important, he was not afraid of silence.

"It's more than impressive. I've never seen anything like it."

On our walk we skirted a basketball court full of shouts, a dumbbell area filled with grunts and growls, and as we passed an exercise room with a large "X" painted on its glass door, my trainer said, "The truth can be found in there." Now we stood at a glass wall and beyond it were the pool and the saunas.

As we watched two men swimming laps, Jon turned to me. "If it's acceptable, we'll begin this Friday evening at seven. You should come early so you can change and be ready to start."

"No, we'll have to postpone. I have a date Friday night." That's what I wanted to say. I guess Jon had just assumed I'd be free. But then I quickly decided not to play games.

I'd learned that games caused lyrical relationships to end on sour notes when one person chose not to play in harmony, or when the partners decided to play discordantly.

I thought I'd heard the opening chords of a symphony with this man so I wanted this relationship to be clean from the beginning. I had no date and lying about it to save face would only cost me more than I could possibly gain. And maybe Jon had only thought I'd be anxious to start.

So I said, "Friday will be fine. I'll be here. Sharp." I resisted the urge to salute again.

"Good. Now, the women's locker room is down that hall." He pointed.

I took a quick look. Everything was luxurious and met with my approval. And as I eased past the crowded areas and out, I was very glad I hadn't glimpsed the ancient sinks and showers.

On our return to the front desk, a female trainer approached. Her age was uncertain, but she was older than Jon. She had a radiant complexion and short brown hair with wisps of gray. Medium-sized, her toned body showed no sagging and her skin was smooth and firm.

"Hi Irene," Jon said.

"Hi there yourself. Is this your new client?" Her no-nonsense eyes looked right into mine.

"Yes, it is. This is Diana. We start Friday."

"I'm ready to go," I said. "I want changes and this is a good way to begin."

"Well, you'll end up changing more than your appearance if you listen to him." This was accompanied by a thumb-jerk toward Jon.

"What do you mean?"

"Come see me sometime and we'll talk gal-to-gal about what's important."

Jon grinned as Irene walked away. "Don't mind her. She thinks I'm mysterious and wants to know more."

While I walked to my car, and dodged a backing truck, all my thoughts were on my exciting new trainer. Jon was intelligent, well-mannered, very hot, and yes, a little mysterious. But he was a good kind of mystery. One I'd love to solve.

# Chapter Three: A Pair of Promises

*"Pride isn't necessary for a happy life."*

*I've* always had a problem with close personal examination. Even in high school I'd thought my hair was too thin, my eyebrows too full, and my lips not full enough, so tonight as I watched two slender women bent over the sinks, their shiny shorts stretched smooth over enviable bottoms, all my old feelings of embarrassment returned. I even hurried through monthly breast exams although I'd allow a special boyfriend to take as long as he liked—in the dark. It didn't make sense, but I knew this self-consciousness came from my childhood when my mother's self-esteem always made sure I was dressed to perfection, and I couldn't seem to overcome it.

Unable to wait until Friday I'd returned to Four Palms mid-week and mistakenly decided to change in one of the toilet stalls. As I struggled I wondered why office wear was designed to torture women. The Egyptians must have invented pantyhose because they mummified and only the dead should have to wear them. But I knew if I didn't wear hose Mr. Dawl would see it as a come-on.

Redressed, I jammed my shed work skin into my locker. The blondes had gone out to the main gym area so I stared into the mirror at myself.

I'd always had a face that looked a little full, even when I was thin. It wasn't full in a round kind of way, but just had a puff under the chin, a bulge to the lower cheek. I'd never look gaunt, no matter how hard I tried. But I liked my nose. It was symmetrical, had never been broken, and suited me. My wavy brown hair always seemed to be in need of a little touch-up, but all in all, it wasn't too bad either.

Then I looked at my profile. No enviable bottom, yet. And as I used my hands to smooth my loose shirt down over my breasts, stomach, and hips, I mentally subtracted all the places I wanted to be smaller and smoother. Finally I sighed, flipped my workout towel over my shoulder and then turned—and stepped on a woman's foot. I hadn't noticed her come up beside me.

"Excuse me! May I help you?" I said using my work telephone voice, the voice that defied anyone to say anything foolish, as I saw a short woman with moist eyes. She looked desperate.

"Probably not," she answered. "I have to go home to my husband and I'm afraid he'll be drunk and upset."

"He wouldn't hurt you?"

"No, but it's the not knowing," she said as she looked at her feet.

I'd never been married and was a little unsympathetic. "Well, I don't have any advice for you." I stated with a sterner voice than I'd intended as I moved toward the locker room door.

"I didn't want your advice," she called after me. "All I wanted was a kind word."

By the time I entered the workout area I felt guilty. I took several breaths and vowed I'd be more pleasant next time.

✳

"Hey there, girl!"

I'd been biking, glad I didn't have to watch out for cars, and was surprised.

"Long time, no see!" Andrea said as she sat on the next bicycle and pedaled. "I'm glad you're okay. You just disappeared. *Poof!*" She gestured.

"I know. I went back to work and I've been worn out ever since."

"I thought that's what happened. So what else is new?"

"Well, I start training on Friday."

"This Friday? I thought you were lusting after him and you've waited all this time to get together?" Her face was quizzical. "You're lucky it was hard to get rid of Larry or you would have been minus one trainer." She creased her forehead.

"Andrea, I've been meaning…"

"I know. To talk to me. I'm sorry, but I had to say something. Jon asked and asked, so I told him what happened. Larry overheard and of course told everyone else. That's one reason he had to go."

"Well, I'm not happy, but let's just forget it. So tell me, what happened to him?" I hoped for a good story.

"One evening I was in here," Andrea began, "and this strange man asked me to go out with him and do certain intimate things and I thought: how does he know those secrets? Then I found out the guys got drunk one night and compared girls. Well, some things shouldn't be shared. Period. Besides, Larry's teeth left bruises on my neck and even gloss couldn't hide my chewed lips. When I get my electric razor and CD's back, he's gone."

As usual she said this as if her experiences happened to everyone.

But Andrea quieted after her mental combat. "I do like coming here. The male scenery is easy on the eyes and I'm starting to see things move around on my body. Plus I have tons of energy and you will too. That is, if you don't sit around in your apartment reading or cooking."

I didn't want to talk about me. "Maybe you should go out with Jim."

She looked at the trainer area. "No, I don't think so."

"Why? He seems nice."

"There's one big reason. He wears those silly glasses."

At first, her excuse seemed flimsy, but Andrea was unable to see beyond his glasses to anything else. "You said you were looking for someone kind and sensitive to your needs. Someone who would appreciate you and not just for your appearance."

"I am, but it's hard to find that someone."

"How do you know it's not Jim? Wearing glasses doesn't change his insides."

"Maybe. But I'm tired of men who only want my outsides and ignore my heart and mind. If they can do it, so can I."

"No one ever wins that way," I said.

"Yes, but that's the way things are. Besides, there's no time to get to know anyone. It's like fast food. If you order anything different than what's offered you won't get served or you wait forever, but if you eat at enough restaurants you'll find one you like and where they'll treat you right."

I'd never considered relationships in quite that way, but she was convinced her logic was correct.

"Now this trainer friend of yours, he's four-star." Andrea looked thoughtful again.

"I know. And I don't want to scare him away. Sometimes I think men wouldn't be so afraid of commitment if women didn't demand it after the second date."

"Like men and sex."

We both laughed.

"True. True," I said. "But seriously, people always talk about what they want in relationships, but what they say isn't what they want at all."

She shrugged.

"Anyway, who's next?" I asked. "You told me you met someone interesting on the Internet."

"Interesting is right! But I can't tell you about him right now."

"Why not?"

"Look who's here!"

It was Jon! Even though part of my mind knew he worked there, another part of me thought he should be there only when I was supposed to be there. He went into the office.

"Go see him!"

"No. He's busy. He has things to do."

"You're right. He's busy thinking about you!"

"How do you know?" She couldn't, but I wanted it to be so.

"Just a hunch. Go tell him you can't figure out how to use the bike."

"I already know how. Yours is the one not on."

"If I pedal fast, I get all sweaty and have to leave. Now...go on!" She started to dismount.

"Okay! Okay!"

I got off and walked carefully down the stairs.

Jon sat with his back to the door and talked on the phone. I heard him say, "Don't let clinging get in the way of having fun." He listened, then replied, "That's right, don't be attached to expectations." And then, "You're welcome. Goodbye." He turned his head and happy surprise lit his face.

But as I stood expectantly in the doorway I felt naked. A mixture of fear and arousal, fused with anticipation, suddenly ignited. It sucked the thoughts from my brain, the liquid from my mouth, and the air from my lungs. Even my knees were sweating. It was the way he looked at me—not with lust, but with peace.

"It's good to see you, Diana." The deep notes in his voice echoed off the metal cabinets.

Wow, good to see *me*...

"Since you're here tonight would you like to take measurements?"

"Do what?"

"We need to establish a baseline so we'll be able to chart your progress. If we can accomplish this tonight then on Friday we can begin your workout promptly at seven."

Wait a minute! I began to roast inside my clothes, inside my mind. I wished I'd stayed on the bike. Was he talking about the usual measurements of interest to men? My stomach fluttered.

Jon removed some instruments from a drawer. Then he said the most horrible words a man can say to a woman, "Please stand on the scale and I'll record your weight."

Immediately the image of an old Halloween card flew into my mind. On the front was a horrified woman shrieking in terror, hair standing on end, tongue protruding from her wide-open mouth, and her bloodshot eyes bulging. Inside was a picture of a scale.

I tried to appear composed and stepped up. But before Jon adjusted the sliding pieces he picked up a pair of scissors, lifted my ponytail, and snipped. I almost screamed!

He placed the tee shirt price tag on the desk and adjusted the scale's measuring pieces until my deepest secret was revealed. He wrote it down without comment and asked me to stand with my arms by my sides

"I need to measure your body fat percentage," he said as he picked up a large white claw. He clicked it open and closed.

"Will it hurt?" I stammered. I didn't know how to measure body fat.

"It might hurt your pride, but that's all. And pride isn't necessary for a happy life."

As I sucked in everything I could, I found it hard to breathe. This was the worst thing that could happen. Now Jon would know exactly how undesirable I was. It would be quantified on his clipboard.

"These calipers will gently pinch the skin. I'll take three readings, one on the back of your arm, one on your back next to your shoulder blade, the third from the side of your torso. Then I'll add the numbers and compare them to a table in this reference book."

He took the measurements doctor-style. No peeking, no subtle brushings. Then the deed was done. Now I would suffer the consequences.

"Diana, for your height and weight," he said, "you have 35% body fat. This places you in the unhealthy category."

"Unhealthy category?" Concern tinged my question. No…it was panic.

"Yes. Your body is composed of two types of weight. Fat body weight is the weight of the fat content of your body. Lean body weight includes everything that isn't fat: your bones, organs, muscles, etc. So at 35%, you have over one-third fat body weight. To convert this percentage to actual pounds of fat, multiply 0.35 by your total weight, the number from the scale."

I tried to do the math in my head, but I didn't like my approximations.

"Our program will reduce that fat percentage in addition to strengthening your muscles and improving your cardiovascular health."

As Jon talked, all I focused on was the word unhealthy. The rest of his words faded away. He must have trained other unhealthy people, but I looked down to hide the tears. From fire to water.

I knew I needed work. My mother, grandmother, and my friends, both male and female, had told me this over and over. Andrea always said, "You have too much jiggle to your wiggle, too many bumps on your curves." How could I not have known? And I knew if I didn't get myself in shape and get desirable, no one would ever find me important enough to stay, and if no one ever stayed, I would be alone. Always.

When I finally looked up, Jon said, "I know you're thinking that there's no hope and that you'll never be good enough to please others whom you feel need to be pleased. But Diana, if you promise me your best efforts, with no excuses and no giving up, I promise you a new person inside and out, and you'll discover truths about yourself and your world that will set you free."

"Free?" I said softly.

"Free from dissatisfaction and unhappiness. Every day you'll be a blooming rose, relieved of its thorns, but not its beautiful scent. You can never be what others say you should be and that won't matter. You will be happy in your own body with health, serenity, and contentment."

As I listened to Jon's vision of what could be I realized that at least once in a person's lifetime there occurs a clear moment of choice, a point at which they see two paths ahead. It could be scary because whichever way they choose will have a profound effect on them. But it could also be exciting!

In a heartbeat, I knew this was such a moment. I could go back to what I had—an unhealed wound. Or I could work with this man and create a real future for myself. I heard the voice within, "Choose the new, let go of the old."

"Okay. I promise to work with you."

It was the calm after an emotional storm. I felt drained, but clean.

"Good," Jon said. "And I won't let you down. Call anytime. At first there may not be much to talk over, but as we progress there will be a lot."

He finished my measurements, took my blood pressure and resting pulse rate. Then he checked my posture and range of motion looking for muscle imbalance.

"We'll develop a program to correct those," he said. "It's mostly biomechanical from too much sitting at work and in the car."

He checked for my doctor's permission and when he was finished and everything was written on his pad, he said, "You've made an important decision tonight, Diana. There'll be stones and holes, but we'll step over and around them. I'm looking forward to seeing you again."

Wrung out, I trudged from the office. Andrea waved from her bike and I couldn't tell if she was smiling, or laughing. It didn't matter. I had more important things to think about.

# Chapter Four: The Preciousness of Life

*"The joy of life is all around if we could but perceive—and believe."*

*"Yes!"* I said as I quietly clapped my hands. I was in my office and had gotten good news. What a wonderful Friday afternoon! Mr. Dawl and his boss had left early for an important business meeting at a gentleman's club and because they were regulars, they wouldn't return before quitting time. For me that meant no working late. Hooray!

I drove to the gym, carefully, and changed. I was early and offered a seat in Jon's office.

"I'd like to go over a few more things."

Gosh, what else could there be? The measurements were finished, but whatever it was, he looked serious.

"I want you to understand," he said, "that as we mature we become accustomed to a pattern of aging based on our individual lifestyles. We live healthy or not so healthy.

"Then when people finally decide to get in shape, many sign-up at a gym where they try to undo in a few workouts a long period of sedentary habits. They do too many exercises per session, use too much weight, and move the weights around too quickly. They also overexert themselves on cardio. What they don't understand is the body and mind team doesn't want to have its habits changed, so it soon calls a halt."

"Calls a halt? How?"

"First, muscle soreness and joint stiffness come from the rapid increase in movement. Then a new diet usually results in changes to digestion and elimination. And there are unconscious shifts in breathing patterns. When those all occur in rapid succession, the body says, "I don't like these changes. I might not survive." Then acting on subconscious signals of fear, an inner voice says, 'You have too much to do to go to the gym.' 'You're too tired to go.' 'Exercise isn't doing you any good.' Or a different voice seductively says, 'You exercised, so have that high-calorie treat.'

"Even my mother fell for the last one. Her doctor prescribed exercise to lower her weight and cholesterol levels. But after a few months, she'd made no progress. I was baffled. Then one day she let it slip. After her session, she'd go to her favorite breakfast spot and treat herself to a ham, egg, and cheese biscuit, a stack of hash browns, and a tall coffee with cream and sugar." Jon shook his head.

"You aren't going to make rapid changes to your body and mind without experiencing resistance. So after a few high velocity times at the gym, the excuses add up and the person wants to quit trying. Few can overcome the body-mind team when it wants to return to its previous pattern of living. Or dying."

That was a lot to absorb. What a reward for being early for my workout! And when I thought it was over, he began again.

"Also, if you lose weight or reduce fat percentage too fast on an unbalanced diet, the body can drop into starvation mode. Then the mind triggers you to stop this perceived starvation. It's a survival technique so as soon as the plan ends, unless you're very careful, the body quickly replaces the lost pounds to protect itself against any possible future starvation. And when those lost pounds return, they usually bring along their friends."

"That's happened to me, and faster than I thought it could."

"That's why it's so important to start an exercise program slowly and not to stop," Jon said. "The body accepts gradual and deliberate changes. But if you go too fast, it's rebellion followed by failure.

"I'm explaining this," he continued, "so you'll see why trainers have a quandary. People want to get fit fast. But how do you tell a person it takes time and there may not be much visible change after only a few workouts? A professional trainer won't push a client because they're aware of the possibility for injury. But if the client doesn't get quick improvements, they think their money was wasted, their mind says, "Quit," and the trainer never sees them again.

"It takes continuous and persistent work to improve the body-mind system, but it can be done and the results are worth it. Good health underlies everything else in life," he concluded, and then stood.

"Now it's time to begin!"

"We're going to start easy," Jon said at the exercise bikes. "You may not think you're getting a workout, but you'll feel it later so don't overdo."

He told me to arrive early so I could warm-up for ten minutes on the bike. He also told me that when I wasn't at the gym, I could burn calories by walking on the beach, swimming, canoeing, bicycling at old Fort Desoto Park, or even going out dancing. And all that was free.

During my warm-up, I sweated like a dumpling in a steamer and when I was finished the panel showed I'd burned exactly 39 calories.

That number seemed low to me. Earlier, I'd inhaled a 250-calorie brownie I'd made the night before and taken to work. And doing the subtraction, I decided this wasn't going to be easy.

"Now," Jon said. "Let's see you really sweat!"

I groaned loud enough for him to hear.

✳

When we arrived at the first exercise machine Jon explained my workout program would include a warm-up for conditioning my muscles, stretching for flexibility, and an hour of resistance training to build and tone. The session would end with a relaxation stretch and twenty minutes of cardiovascular exercise. He would track my progress by recording every workout on his form.

"Tonight we'll work your chest muscles and triceps," he said. "The second session will be the back muscles and biceps. In the third session, it will be the muscles of your thighs and legs. Then we'll have entire workouts devoted to the abdominals."

I'd been dreading this moment. Now I'd be able to demonstrate how weak and uncoordinated I was and also how little I knew about my body.

"I don't know how to use these machines!" I admitted in a panic as I looked around. There were so many!

"That's why I'm here," he said.

Jon told me to check the machines' cables for breaks or frays, to never use more weight than I could handle, and to remember that I controlled the weight. If the weight was controlling me, then there was too much. Also, I was to be seated firmly and to be certain any adjustable part was at the correct position for me. I should raise and lower the weights using a rhythm tied to my normal breathing: exhale as I raised the weight and inhale as I lowered the weight. And to get the most out of my repetitions it was time in tension. The longer my muscle fibers were under load, the harder they would work.

"I know these are a lot of rules," he concluded, "but, as in all of life, you want to avoid injuries."

My first exercise was on the Chest Press machine. I did what he called three sets, which were ten repetitions each. I could barely finish, but Jon stood close by and counted, encouraged me, and made certain I exercised correctly.

After a brief rest, we moved to several other machines. First was the Pec Flye Deck that imitated flying and I discovered that being a bird must be harder than I'd imagined. Next on the Overhead Press, I pretended I was Superwoman as I pushed my arms upward, but I was certain she could have lifted more than twenty pounds. At the Cable Crossover, I learned where grunting sounds came from. And then I did the standing Triceps Pull Down, and used the sitting Triceps Press Down. When I finished, I stretched again and then somehow managed to bike for twenty minutes.

Dripping with sweat, I studied Jon's profile while he sat on an adjacent bicycle and reviewed my program. I was impressed. He'd stayed with me the entire time and hadn't been distracted by any gym-bunnies.

When I'd dismounted, Jon said, "My purpose is to show you how to develop a healthy lifestyle, get your body back in balance, and how to maintain it.

"But I'd like to go beyond all that. In addition to the physical, there's the mental aspect to well being. I'd also like to teach you certain universal truths, which if applied with diligence, can yield a happy life, one free from dissatisfaction and anxiety. We could begin with a discussion about the preciousness of life, if you're interested and would like to have coffee with me."

As I listened to his words a gear clicked and a mental door snapped open. Blue-white radiance poured through this crack and painted a vertical stripe from my head to my toes dividing my body and mind. One half said, "This is what you've wished for; this is the way to have the life of your dreams." The other half said, "Why me? I only came here to get thin and boring talk won't make me sexy."

But negative thoughts like that had held me back for so long and I knew they had to be banished. Many times before I'd tried to let them go, and then backed away. Maybe Jon understood how to let go and could teach me to understand it. Still, I knew when I released the old patterns it would be like ripping a bandage off a scab, but if I could stand the moment of pain, relief would come much faster. So I had a choice. I could open the door further, or I could kick it shut. It took only a moment. I reached out and grasped the door's rough edge.

"You've made your decision?" Jon asked. He knew there'd been a battle for my life.

"Yes, I have. I *am* interested. And I'd love to have coffee with you." And with a single phrase, a simple choice—my world changed.

Tonight I was glad the coffee house had booths along one wall where it was quiet. On the way in the car I'd hidden my cheek and nose shine and added lots more deodorant. I thought about lipstick, but decided none tonight. I was tired, but also excited.

Jon arrived a few minutes later and I was surprised when he appeared in a white, long-sleeved shirt, black jeans, and dark shoes. He stood tall, chest out, and he moved with a smooth casualness. I saw the outlines of his shoulder and arm muscles flexing and a few hairs peeked out from his open collar. I couldn't see his rear. Yet.

"It's me," he said. "I dress regularly in the outside world."

His clothes weren't my thoughts.

We ordered decafs with skim milk.

After a few minutes of sipping, I said, "You know about me, now tell me something about you."

"I plan to," he said, "Later. First, I need to explain something. I rarely see female clients outside the gym and I don't want you to get the wrong idea."

"What wrong idea?"

"The idea that you fell for a line I'd cooked up to get a different kind of workout session. I don't want to compromise your trust, and you must understand I have your best destiny in mind. If this isn't clear, our time together will be wasted."

I felt a brief touch of resentment. I knew how to keep men away. But I saw his concern, he wanted me to feel safe. And I couldn't remember a man who'd put my interests ahead of his own. Maybe he *was* different.

"I promise I'll keep my distance."

"Sure," he said. "But only one coffee. And no cream, I don't want you to get carried away."

"Okay," I laughed. "So now you can tell me something about you." I leaned forward.

"How about I tell you something compelling about life instead? Did you know your life is a set of parentheses in eternity?" Jon said, his smiling eyes looking deep into mine.

I blinked. I couldn't help it.

"They open at your birth and close when you die. Within your parentheses is the most wonderful of all things—your unique trip through time and space. What a miraculous and precious journey! How fortunate it is simply to be alive! Many things could have prevented your birth and yet here you are."

"Hmm."

His dark hair was nicely combed and just touched the tops of his ears. There was no grey, but I knew he must be older than me.

"At birth," he continued, "your body was endowed with a set of senses. They are your gateways to the world and form the basis of all your experiences. To be able to interact with the world through the open doorways of the senses is where the enjoyment of life comes from."

That's true. I placed my hands under my chin and stared at his face. He had such pretty eyes, half-mooned shaped with slight hints of lines, and unable to do anything but smile. They were so alive, and so...well...seductive. And I wished I had his long lashes, but they must have come with his eyes. Mine were short, fringing my dark brown eyes.

"When your senses contact things, mental and physical feelings arise," Jon said, "and the perceptions that come from those feelings are what give rise to your thoughts. The same feelings also create and maintain your memories."

"I didn't realize that." In truth, I'd never thought about it before.

"And did you know your thoughts control your life? They give it direction and it's from them that all your happiness and sadness arise. If you act or speak from unskillful thoughts, unhappiness will follow. However, if you act or speak from skillful thoughts, happiness will follow you closely."

As I listened, his voice was melodic and soothing to me. I'd never heard anyone talk about those things like he did. But it was his moist, soft lips that hypnotized me while I watched them move.

Jon continued, "Skillful thoughts increase peace and happiness; unskillful thoughts do the opposite. Understand?"

I nodded. I understood, maybe. And I hoped he couldn't tell that my attention kept wandering as I studied his slender hands, ring-less, resting relaxed in front of him on the table.

"Joining together your body, your senses, your feelings, and your thoughts, is your consciousness. Consciousness tells you that you're alive and awake. It's the total awareness of who you are and your place in the world. It is the culmination of everything else. With the conscious knowledge of "I," you recognize yourself and know that you think.

"I'll give you an example. In the morning when you wake from the sleep of unconsciousness, your senses reach out and give you information on the surrounding conditions and the state of your body. From those contacts, feelings of pleasure, displeasure, or indifference arise. Then from your thoughts and memories, who you are and where you are dawns in your consciousness and you determine if it's a good day, a bad day, or an 'I don't care' day. And finally from that knowledge you choose how to live it."

He paused and looked at me as if expecting a comment. The best I could do was, "If all that goes on, it must happen fast."

"It does. Everything has been checked out and decided before you get out of bed."

After a pause, Jon continued, "Long ago a sage was asked, 'What is the most amazing thing you know?' The sage answered, 'All around me I see people watching others who are aging, getting sick, and dying, and they think it will never happen to them.'"

"I've heard more pleasant stories," I said.

"True, but the point is you don't know how many days you have on your journey, especially healthy ones, so every one of them should be a valuable gem.

"We begin in the timeless manner of children, but this shifts. We come to see life as a struggle and lose sight of how special being alive truly is. In our hurry to conform, we become wrapped in dramas and forget how fragile our lives are. Being alive is a gift, but it's a gift that can be taken away."

"I try not to think about that part." I'd pulled my attention away from his face and about how much I'd like it closer to mine, and now focused on Jon's words.

"I'm telling you to make a point. You've made an excellent decision. You're going to get your body into shape and you're going to take better care of it. This will slow the aging process and reduce physical problems thus increasing your total number of healthy days.

"Your body is the only vehicle you have for your senses, the only coach to carry you through the world. If it is mistreated or worn without thought to its care, it will break down and eventually become unusable. When that happens, there's no trade-in. There's nowhere else for you to go. If you understand the preciousness and brevity of vitality, you'll prioritize your health and safety. The fit body with its senses forms the base for happy and joyful living and that's where we start our journey."

"So I shouldn't worry that I'll get sick and die someday," I said. "I should concentrate on making wholesome living a priority and my life will be pleasant to the end."

"Right, but there's more," he said. "Cleaning up your body, the temple of your consciousness is just the first step. Let me use an analogy. You are like a horse and carriage. The carriage is your body, the horse is your emotions, and your mind is the driver. And you are the owner. When the first three are working together you have a smooth ride, but if one or more gets out of control, then watch out or you'll end up in a ditch. We've started with your body. Later, the mind and emotions."

"Isn't it hard getting them to all work together? How do you do it?"

"My life wasn't always serene," Jon said. "My mind was in charge and I was never at peace. I'd worn myself out grasping for golden rings that only turned to rust.

"Then after a long while, I realized I didn't have to live in pain and fear. But only if I chose to make it so. It became a matter of desire and belief. If I desired to change, but didn't believe I could,

I'd have no success. Or, if I believed I could change, but had no desire, then again I'd have no success.

"But I believed my life could be free from suffering. And the desire for serenity burned white hot. So I chose a different way, just as you have, Diana, and today I'm happy and peaceful most of the time. I still have much to learn, but I've found that I want to teach what I know in the way it was taught to me because knowledge is always to be passed along, and truths are always to be shared. Then others can have what I have and gain it in less time and with fewer struggles. Why let someone else suffer from the same affliction?"

"You're right. But how much is, 'most of the time'?" I asked.

"About ninety percent," Jon answered. "This is a human incarnation and I do the best I can. But my aim is not, nor do I expect, perfection. And question me. Don't just take my word. You must prove the teachings for yourself or they are valueless."

"But how can you teach me to be happy and content?"

"What I'll do is give you tools, explain their use, and point the way. But *you* must build the life you want, Diana. Then it will be yours and no one can ever take it away."

"But if everyone wants to be joyful, then how does it get so mixed up?"

"What's lacking is belief," Jon said. "Pressures in the lives of men and women squeeze them and their belief in happiness is wrung out. It's like taking a sponge dripping with goodness and love and wringing out every last drop. But thinking there's no bliss is wrong. The joy of life is all around if we could but perceive—and believe."

There was silence, and then he asked if I had any questions.

All I could muster was, "How did you begin teaching?"

Jon's answer was simple. "It's said, 'when the student is ready, the teacher appears.' But it also works in reverse: when the teacher is ready, the student appears."

While I drove home, my body fatigued and my mind awhirl, I thought about my life, about how this wasn't the evening I'd expected, about how fascinating he was, and about how Jon's words rang true.

Later as I drifted off to sleep, I saw my thoughts as balloons. I let the bad ones fly free and netted the good ones. I saw how precious I was. My breathing slowed, "I believe...I believe..."

# Chapter Five: Bold Traveler

*"It takes dedication—and a strong back—to be a Bold Traveler in your life."*

"**Come** on! Tell me!" Andrea pleaded. "So you worked out and then went for coffee?"

"Yes," I said. Monday's lunch was at a pasta-salad-soup cafeteria. I was wilted and soggy-minded.

"And then?"

"That's all there is to tell." Sometimes I thought Andrea needed a more dramatic friend, one who had exciting episodes to share. I'd been in tragic scenes before and had found that when you shared those tearjerkers with your friends, it was only a comparison of either how much you got hurt or how much you hurt another, and how you vowed never to repeat it. But the emotional rush was addicting, and after a short time you'd look for a another performance.

I remembered a friend, Carla, and how she'd whined because she could never meet a kind and sensitive man. At last her pleas were heard and such a man appeared. He was quiet, secure in his knowledge of who he was, and treated her with respect.

Then one day Carla came over.

"He sounds terrific," I'd said.

"He was." This was followed by a torrent of tears.

"Was? What happened?"

"We were so happy it seemed like a dream. But then I thought I needed more excitement. So I'd get angry about some little thing, create a drama, and then play it out causing all sorts of upset. Afterwards, when I'd gotten my fix, I'd quickly calm everything down. Then I became the heroine. I had saved the relationship! I only wish I had saved it from me.

"It didn't take many of those episodes to make him look for someone who appreciated him, someone who treated him with respect. And he soon found her." The sloppy, mascara-laden tears continued.

But the thoughts about Carla had jangled a chain and I remembered dropping an old boyfriend. He'd been kind, treated me like gold, and he'd loved me. But I was important and self-righteous. I showed him the power of my anger! How different my life might have been had we stayed together. A sob tore from my gut.

"Take it easy, Diana," Andrea said, startled. "Is there a mouse in your soup? Those vegetables are suspicious. Their edges look nibbled."

I tried to laugh. Whenever strong feelings showed their faces they touched somewhere inside of her where she didn't want to go and so a joke or laughter deflected us away from that place. She wasn't making fun of me. She was only saving herself.

"No mice, Andrea," I said quietly.

"I'm sorry. I didn't mean to joke. You've been there for me. What can I do for you?"

"May I tell you about something? Maybe you can help me to understand it." I had a bad hangover from too much to dream last night.

"Sure. But first eat some soup and salad. You need energy."

"All right," I said and took a greasy mouthful. Mouseful?

✳

Because I didn't have many stories, Andrea was eager.

"It all began when I was looking at Jon's pen. It's black and gold and has cut marks on one side. I put it on the nightstand, turned off the light, and went to sleep. Or at least I thought I went to sleep, but because it all seemed so real, I was never certain.

"When I awoke in my dream, I was alone. I was standing barefoot on a ledge of black rock overlooking a treeless crater ringed by jagged peaks and around me, ice crystals were falling.

"Then I saw a figure in the distance, so I followed a narrow, winding path down to it. As I walked, steam hissed from cracks in the warm rock and hot springs smelled of sulfur. And the whole time, cold gusts of wind were blowing sharp grit into my gown where it itched like biting bugs."

"Where do you get dreams like that?" Andrea said, leaning closer.

I shrugged.

"As I walked towards the hooded figure, who was walking towards me, its face changed. It became a kaleidoscope of people I'd known: relatives, friends, pets, even your face was there."

"Weren't you scared?" she asked, sitting back a little.

"No, not yet. The figure handed me a pen like my trainer's and then vanished. And as I looked down at it, the cuts became letters."

"What did they spell?"

"Only two words: Bold Traveler."

"What does *that* mean?"

"I'm not sure. Let me finish."

"Then the rock under my feet changed into a crystal stairway and as I crept down it, the light weakened and the air warmed. At the bottom, a narrow hallway of arches led me to a huge room where the whitish, curved walls and ceiling were covered with thin cracks. A glowing red cavity filled most the floor and there were white sparks in the hot air above it. I stripped and sat down with my back to the wall."

"You took off all your clothes?" Her mauve manicure masked her open mouth.

"Yes, and it was quiet, except for hissing. But as my eyes adjusted to the low light, I saw that there were even more white sparks than before. Then they swarmed around me...and one touched my bare skin.

"As it burned me, an image appeared over the cavity. It was a childhood memory of stuffed animals and I smiled. Then as a second spark touched me, another scene appeared. I was a teenager, yelling at my mother and slamming doors. With another spark, I was eating pizza with friends. And another spark revealed me making love for the first time.

"I saw the scenes go by faster and faster, and as they came closer to the present, the happy ones decreased and I twisted in pain. I saw how I came to be where I am, and it hurt. I wrapped my arms around my knees and closed my eyes. They opened to the loud buzz of the alarm.

"I was on the floor leaning against my bed with my nightgown in shreds. The pen was on the nightstand. I grabbed it, but the marks were unchanged so I threw it down. I wanted to call in sick, but on Mondays, it starts ugly rumors. So here I am."

"You know," Andrea said. "I was so fascinated, I forgot to eat. Well, I can get takee-outee."

"But what do you think my dream means?"

"I don't know, Diana. Ask your trainer friend. It's his pen."

"I might. But in daylight, it seems silly."

"Silly or not, it's something to talk about the next time you see him. Which is tonight, right?"

＊

The afternoon evaporated and then it was workout time. I was prompt and ready.

"Warm up first." Jon pointed to the bikes. "If you don't remember what to do, let me know. I'll come over in ten minutes," he called as I walked away.

It began with an ember of resentment. "Don't remember what to do?" Did I sound stupid when we were talking? Maybe he didn't know who he was dealing with! I'm smart and practically in charge of my department. And I'm paying *him*!

As my indignation rose, expectations of a happy workout together withered and my mind wrapped itself in hot-towel thoughts. Already sweating, I adjusted the seat, pedaled, and jabbed the start button. I'll show him! But when I set the program, the girl on the next bike overwhelmed me with her stench as she pumped and then squirted me with water as she slurped it into her ugly mouth. That distracted me. Then the effort needed to turn the pedals increased and increased and increased.

There must be something wrong with me, I thought. I'm working much harder than last time. Maybe my crazy dream had worn me out. Maybe I'd forgotten to take my vitamins this morning as I hurried out of my apartment choking down a breakfast burrito that was cold in the center. This exercise program was not going to work. Sweat poured down my face as heavy sadness filled my heaving chest. My plans were over. No shapeliness. No nothing.

"Whoa! What are you doing? Stop!" My trainer was beside me. "We're starting slow. Remember?" Jon's eyes questioned my liquid-filled ones.

"I was following *your* instructions."

"Last time you started at Level One. It's a big jump to go from Level One to Level Seven.

"It's on Level Seven? No wonder it's so hard!"

"Yes. I saw you panting and came right over. Cool down for five minutes," he said, setting the bike's resistance to the lowest level.

Relief washed over me. I'd gotten angry at an attack on my wonderfulness and had gotten careless. I'd created my own problem and my mind had magnified the whole thing. Anger and its partner despair had almost cost me, again. I was the only person I knew who could have road rage on a stationary bicycle.

"Can we still workout?" I asked. "Please?"

"Of course," he said.

"Tonight's back and biceps night," Jon announced as we went to a tall, square-framed machine with a center weight stack.

On one side was the Lat Pull Down. Seated, I pulled a horizontal bar down from over my head until it almost touched the top of my chest and then allowed the weights to raise it again. On the opposite side was the Low Row where I sat and, while keeping my back flat, leaned forward, pulled the chrome grips inward to my body, and then slowly released them. Then I used the High Row machine where I sucked in my stomach and did all my sets with a minimum of grumbles.

When I finished, I said, "I could have lifted more weight."

"I'm sure you could, but remember we're starting slow because we want minimum resistance from the body and mind, and no injuries. If you use too much weight or move it too fast, you may exceed the muscular strength needed to stop its motion. This results in injury to the muscles, tendons, and ligaments, and to the capsule of a joint. You could get a muscle strain or sprain, or in severe cases, damage to a joint, like the hip, knee, or shoulder.

"And total relief might never occur. Ask anyone who's had joint trauma and they'll say it wasn't worth it, although you'll find others who treat injuries as a badge of gym courage.

"As we mature, we become more and more familiar with bodily discomfort, so there is no need to experience it sooner than necessary. Remember that you workout with others, but only you feel the pain. And people believe it can't happen to them."

"I'll be careful," I said.

"And I'll make sure you are. Now, let's do One-arm Dumbbell Rows." And as Jon led the way to the free weight area, he explained, "The term 'free weight' means the weights are not attached to any piece of exercise equipment."

When we arrived, I saw everyone was dressed to expose large amounts of skin. At first I thought they were vain, but then I realized they were proud. And they had to see their muscles to work them correctly.

In contrast, I was in my oversized gym outfit and looked like a clown. All I needed was a big red nose. And although no one seemed to pay any attention, I was certain I saw sly glances in the mirrors.

After Jon's instructions and my first attempts with the Dumbbell Rows, I said, "This feels different than a machine."

"Exercise machines mostly operate in one plane of motion." He demonstrated with his arm. "Free weights recruit more muscle fibers and require other muscles to work together for balance and coordination. They mimic how things work out in the world."

Between sets, I watched a man dressed in a sleeveless red muscle shirt and black, form-fitting bicycle pants load three forty-five-pound plates onto a bar that stuck out from the front of a machine. Then he leaned forward on an inclined pad, reached down and grasped two handles, and lifted and lowered the weighted bar.

"What's that bicycle pants man doing?" I asked.

"He's using a machine for adding thickness and definition to the muscles of the middle back. It's called a donkey dong."

I could see why and tried not to stare.

"One final exercise," Jon said. "With my assistance, you're going to do Bicep Curls with a barbell. Widen your feet, tuck your elbows into your sides, and hold your hands out, palms up. Lower the bar nearly to your thighs and then slowly curl it upward. Keep your elbows close to your body and motionless. When you reach the top, slowly lower the bar back down."

My muscles burned, but I finished. I was drenched in sweat and had a very strong aroma, different from any before. As Jon finished his notations and said he'd see me next time, I told him how grateful I was.

Then I did my stretches and cardio, and later as I got my bag out of my locker, Irene came over.

"Good workout!" she said. "How'd you get Jon for your trainer?"

"I don't know. He chose me."

"If Jon chose you, you must be special. He only works with a few clients. Management wants him to take on more, but he won't do it unless he believes he can help. So you have to be dedicated."

"Thanks for telling me. I appreciate it."

As I walked to my car, I knew she was right. It takes dedication—and a strong back—to be a Bold Traveler in your life.

# Chapter Six: An Off Day

*"Finding someone who's in the world, but not of it, doesn't happen often."*

"Wake up, brown eyes!" Andrea chirped, after the phone's ring shattered my senses. "Let's go shopping! Or are you pumping with your trainer?"

"I'm awake, Andrea! Why are you up so soon?" I collapsed on the bed. My heartbeat slowed; my muscles ached.

"I've decided to get up earlier on weekends because if you sleep until noon there's no day left. And if you have someone over it takes him forever to leave and then there's no time before you have to get ready for Saturday night. It's my new promise and I'm spending the extra time with you. When can you be ready?"

Darn. I'd wanted to stay home with my hair in a ponytail and wear my nightshirt all day. I'd watch movies, read, and maybe try a new recipe. But now..."I can meet you in ninety minutes."

"Thirty. I'm ready."

"Sixty, minimum."

"Okay. I'll see you in an hour at the crepe shop. If you're late, I'm ordering without you. 'Bye!"

✳

Barefaced and sensibly dressed, I breakfasted on crepes with a touch of maple syrup. They used the real, uncut stuff and its delicious thickness coated my tongue in the most erotic way.

Larry was gone for good, her razor was ruined, and on the CD's were love notes written in red felt-tipped pen, substituting a *w* for the second *a* in Andrea's name.

"So tell me," she said. "You and your trainer…?"

"We're taking it slow." I didn't know how we were taking it.

"Well, you better speed things up because tonight's Good Ol' Saturday Night. Date night for *some* and you'll be floundering at home reading paperbacks and eating stale sushi."

"No thanks," I said with a little dejection. "Hurry up and finish your blintzes."

She made a face; the blintzes vanished.

Then we strolled about and looked in the shops. Andrea purchased a sheer pink robe and gold sandals. I bought a pair of shower shoes, a new workout towel, and some stronger deodorant.

In a small perfume store she acquired a fresh bottle of the "Persuader," her secret weapon, and insisted I take a sample. Later we said our goodbyes. She had to get ready for a blind date.

When I arrived at the security gate for my apartments I saw it was imbedded in the side of an old work truck. The owner's middle finger flew in all directions. But as I waited and waited for the two guys from the car in front of me to push open the gate, I had an idea. I could go to the gym! It was only four in the afternoon and I wouldn't look like someone who had nowhere else to go on Saturday night. And maybe *he* would be there.

When I finally cleared the gate, I raced past the cabbage palms, parked, then hurried down the long row of pampas grass, up the steps, and into my cramped two-bedroom apartment. I almost stumbled over the heap of shoes piled just inside the front door and in my closet I kicked aside the stack of laundry and quickly changed clothes. I grabbed my purse, a warm bottle of water, and ran back down to my car. Jon had warned me about over-training, but I wouldn't do that.

✳

When I arrived, Four Palms was strangely quiet.

"I hope I didn't upset you by talking out of turn the other day," Irene said as she mounted an adjacent bike. "Your trainer is a peculiar guy, but nice."

"What you said had the opposite effect," I said, a little surprised. "That's why I'm here. Is Jon around?" I looked over my shoulder and tried not to appear eager.

"He doesn't usually come in on weekends."

"Oh." Visions of stale sushi chopped in my head.

"He reads and studies," she continued. "Must give him those unusual ideas he talks about. My head hurts when I think about everything he tells me."

"Yes, I know. When we went for coffee I thought I was having regular not decaf."

"Oh, so *you're* the one!"

Her comment surprised me. Our coffee date didn't seem unique to me.

"We had coffee and talked. What's wrong with that?"

"Nothing, but Jon's so private," she said. "He's interested in what you say and remembers what you tell him. It's just that after you talk, Jon knows all about you and you don't know anything about him."

Our coffee discussion had seemed open, but I saw she was right, Jon hadn't said much about himself. But as I thought it occurred to me that maybe my trainer was a lot like me—alone and in need of someone to whom he could bear his soul. And I was that someone!

He could confide in me and then I'd be needed! But in the future I'd find Jon was freer than anyone I'd ever known.

"Did you hear me?" Irene poked at my arm. "I have a plan. You draw him out and then tell me if you learn anything interesting. You know, kind of gal to gal."

But as a polite refusal rose, another female trainer appeared.

"Hi Irene!" A glossy, mega-watt smile glimmered in the lights as a slender blonde dressed in a Four Palms shirt and khaki shorts bounced and stepped.

Nice teeth. But with only her two words I'd already formed a dislike.

Before Irene could introduce us, she said, "Have you just started? Do you need a trainer to help with your program?" She looked me over as her smile glowed.

"I already have one."

"You know her trainer, Sarah," Irene said.

Sarah stopped stepping, hands on hips, lips to a line. "The coffee girl."

That gym jungle was small. The monkeys chattered to all the other monkeys.

"Yes. We had coffee and talked," I said.

"About what?"

"Life and things."

"Well, Jon wouldn't have coffee with me," She said with a stomp. "And *I* asked him. Why'd he go with you?"

"I don't know."

"I can't believe that!" She shook her head. "But I know what his problem is. He always asks if we're happy or peaceful. He doesn't seem to understand what goes on between men and women. I'd love to get into his head, and somewhere else too." Pouty smile. "'Bye, Irene." She walked away and down the steps.

"Don't let Sarah bother you," Irene said. "She's working on her Mrs. Trainer degree and she's very proud of what she has to offer."

I nodded. And I wondered if I'd have the courage to ask Jon why he didn't go for coffee, or more, with the bouncy Miss Sarah.

"May I ask you a question, Irene?" I guessed we were on a first name basis. "Why is it calmer in here today? It feels different."

"Saturday people aren't weekday people. They're here because they want to be here."

"Like me?"

"Yes, Diana, like you."

"Weekday evening gym goers fall into different groups," Irene continued as she counted them on her fingers. "First, there's the get rid of stress crowd. They come in to work it off, but their frantic pace really doesn't help them. Second, there's the get healthy fast bunch. They go at their exercises with a vengeance, but despite their good intentions, they burn out quickly. Third, there's the work off the weekend pack. They're why Monday's are always crowded. They work out a bit, sit in the sauna, and go home. Guilt quenched. Then there's the must meet somebody clique. They spend more time talking than working out. Provocative dress is the key, along with lingering looks in the mirrors.

"Lastly, there's a special kind that comes in on Friday evenings. They're the must buff up for my date I might get lucky squad. They pump up their muscles to get them full of blood and bulging. Afterwards, they take hot showers. That's good for the smell, but the hot water relaxes the muscles and helps the blood flow back out. What a dilemma. Be buff and stink, or smell sweet and look weak. Of course they could take a cold shower, but that would defeat their purpose.

"You meet these types over and over again, and not just in the gym," she ended. "So what's your story, young lady?"

I didn't feel that young, but answered, "A friend talked me into coming, and then I was in a car wreck. But since driving into the parking lot that first night, I've felt I belong here. I don't know whether my trainer has anything to do with it, but I suspect he does."

"Maybe Jon's cast a love spell on you," she said with a little smirk.

"No, I don't think that's it." I tried hard to suppress my own smile. "But there's something about him and I want to find out more."

"Can't say I blame you," Irene said. "Strangeness or not, finding someone who's in the world, but not of it, doesn't happen often."

After the bike, I walked toward the free weight area to practice Bicep Curls. But as I got closer I saw a giant of a man in skimpy clothes lying on one of the black benches. His huge hands pumped gigantic dumbbells. I stopped. At bookstores I'd secretly studied men like this in fitness magazines as I pretended to peruse the fashion issues. His massive body shone in the bright lights and his outfit hid next to nothing. He must have worked out for years. My heart raced.

His weights dropped with a heavy thump. Then he sat up and caught me. As he peered into the mirrored wall he saw me watching him pump his iron. His puffy face blossomed.

"Hey!" he said in a rush of breath. "What's your name? You're working with Jon. Want to have a drink? I'm sweating like a pig; I'll have to shower." His panted comments rose and fell with his breathing.

I turned away and aimed at the Low Row machine.

When I looked back, I saw him lift his bulk and trudge after me. His eyes stared at my rear; his hands hung by his sides. Sweat ran down his forehead to his slack mouth as his big chest expanded and contracted. I tried to walk faster without being obvious. I'd hide in the locker room if necessary. A gym troll wanted my body!

Then with a grunted exhale, he turned to the drinking fountain and satiated himself. He let water run over his eyes and snorted it into his nose. The sign above the fountain said not to spit. But there was nothing about cleaning out your eyes and nose.

"Close call," I mumbled, seated on the Low Row bench.

"Did Oscar scare you?" a voice behind me said. For a heartbeat I thought it was my trainer, but when the voice walked around front, I saw it was bicycle pants man, the guy from the donkey dong.

I called him bicycle pants man because every time I saw him, he wore the black, form-fitting shorts of bicyclists. He was triangular with broad shoulders and well-developed biceps. His torso narrowed to slim hips and legs, the upper parts slickly coated in black pants whose color matched his short hair. I'd seen other girls check him out and there he stood next to me.

"He wasn't chasing you," BPM said. "He was just pleased to see you admiring him."

"I wasn't admiring him. I wanted to do Bicep Curls and he was in the way."

"Well, if he'd attacked, I'd have rushed to your rescue since your trainer isn't here. In fact, what are you doing here without him? You could hurt yourself."

I decided against anger. I knew he was goading me so I'd get mad. Then he'd calm me down in a soothing, manly fashion and we'd become pals, and more.

"I could have out run him," I replied. "Besides, he'd need someone with more meat." I had plenty, but didn't think he'd be tactless and point it out.

"You have more than enough to satisfy him," he said with an appraising leer.

I glared.

"But you'll be trim soon," he quickly added. "Jon's a good trainer, even if he tries too hard at being the strong, silent type."

"Well, he talks to me." I was not going to get angry. "He talks about having a serene and fulfilling life."

"I've heard that stuff and some makes sense," BPM said. "But the world isn't that way. You have to work through the pain. It's too bad he won't be here long because he always has something good to say."

"Jon's leaving?" I was alarmed. I'd just started!

"Not yet. He said he had a new friend and wanted to stay. At first, I thought it might be you, but…well…you're not his type."

"I'm not his type?"

"Jon wants someone more…HWP." BPM stared at the "X" room.

"HWP?"

Without looking at me, he explained, "HWP: height and weight proportional, as in proportional to each other."

Rays of understanding penetrated my ignorance. BPM was saying that because I wasn't HWP, my trainer wouldn't be interested. An icy wave of sadness washed over me. I didn't know Jon well, but he'd never given me any reason to think I wasn't attractive. And I'd felt so good around him. I must have forgotten my place. Speechless, I sat and saw nothing.

"Hey, sorry. I didn't mean to offend you. And let's not say anything to Jon. I don't want to upset him too."

My anger finally sparked. Why are men always like that? First exuberant, then secretive. They say, "That was fun, but let's keep it to ourselves." But sometimes it's easier to agree than to argue. I nodded, but my feelings were very hurt.

BPM hurried away and I tried to do a few sets for my chest and back, but my heart wasn't in it so I decided to rest in the dry sauna.

The club had both wet and dry saunas. They were coed so you weren't supposed to go nude, but if you were HWP, I doubted anyone would complain. I changed into my swimsuit and shower shoes, put on a tee shirt, and wrapped up in a towel.

Inside the sauna, the dry heat felt good and my skin tightened pleasantly. As I sat on the upper bench, I saw Oscar walk past the glass door and heard him go into the wet sauna. I closed my eyes. Cacti appeared.

Then the door swished open to admit a HWP girl dressed in a midnight blue bathing suit with two cell phones attached. She had straight black hair, light brown skin, and silver earrings that jingled as she sat.

We had only minutes of quiet before one of the phones buzzed like a snake. She looked at it and answered. It was a missing package. The call was over and the dry silence returned.

Then the other phone rang. The snake was loud, but it was nothing like the ring. We jumped, and as she grabbed for her phone, I remembered a former boyfriend who imitated multi-sound car alarms. A couple of beers and off he went. He even did it in bed.

She answered in Spanish. And after she ended her call she apologized and asked, "How are you getting along?"

"I just started, but I want changes—and soon!"

Emphasis on the soon. I wanted to be HWP like her—and fast!

"They'll come," she said. "You've got my former trainer, so you'll get whatever you need." She smiled a secret smile.

"I'm counting on it, and him." But green sprouted.

"So, what did Jon teach you?"

"One lesson he taught me was how to maintain a happy relationship. It was simple, but it worked. And all I can say is, 'Wow!'"

Lucky her. Being HWP, I couldn't imagine that she would have any trouble with relationships.

Then one of her phones played a symphony. She quickly answered and began to talk about the fun things she planned do with the caller that night.

It was a mirror of my own wishes. I wanted someone to call me while I was lounging in a hot sauna and whisper sweet things. And I found I'd had enough dry sauna and decided to try the wet. Oscar or no Oscar, I was tired of being a wimp.

I slowly opened the glass door and there he was. His bulk slouched in a corner; his towel a loincloth from a gladiator movie. He opened one eye and closed it without speaking. I sat on the lower bench as far away from him as I could. The tiles were hot and moist and I drifted.

A wet popping sound brought me back. Outwardly nothing had changed, but helped by the billowing steam, a smell so rank that it induced instant gagging was filling the room. Oscar had broken wind, as my grandmother would have said.

I gave him a dirty look. He hadn't moved. He hadn't even noticed his own pollution! Then it became unbearable and I nearly fainted in the steamy stench as I fled. I stood by the pool to recover my breath, too blown away to be mad.

And Saturday night or not, I was leaving for the safety of my apartment and its full refrigerator.

# Chapter Seven:
## The Floor of Colored Paper

*"He'd tell me not to tolerate anything that hurt my self-worth."*

*When* you look forward to being with someone and you know they look forward to being with you, disturbing events can almost be ignored.

Wednesday afternoon an important business partner requested an updated manual for our latest software package—immediately. We couldn't send it without approval and Mr. Dawl was out. Susan, his brave secretary, solved our problem by calling one of his lairs. And when he and two others returned from their planning session, our office life degenerated into chaos.

The interruption by the hostess while he watched a shower dance had stewed his mood. Then as he gulped his last drink, he'd spilled gin on the tacky tie he'd gotten from his eight-year-old son last Christmas. This topped off his anger pie and during the impatient drive back to work in an oven-hot car, he was baked.

The manual was ready, but Mr. Dawl wanted changes even though he'd approved the final version that morning. I knew I'd have to cancel my workout so I left the conference room. I didn't see him follow me.

I called Jon from my office and left a message saying that should I finish in time, I'd be there to workout. I didn't want him to think

I was a quitter. Then as I turned around I saw Mr. Dawl in the doorway watching me with a leering look.

"So who was that, Ms. Archer?" he asked with a curl of his lip.

I decided to be honest, though usually I would have hedged. If too much was known about your private life, it was detrimental. Management used the knowledge to slow raises and promotions and I was due for both. Any information was important, especially if they couldn't find problems with your work. It wasn't fair and you could never prove it, but it happened all the time.

"I left a message for my trainer," I replied. "I had a workout scheduled for this evening, but finishing the manual takes priority."

"What kind of workout?" The leer morphed into a sneer. "Is this your new honey, some dumb jock?"

"He's not my honey. He's only my trainer."

"And what's he trained you to do?" His implications were obvious. "Something kinky? You could use some training in how to please a man." His comments tilted the conversation downward.

"I go to the gym to get into better shape, so I can work harder here." I glanced at my tiny office.

"Your work is fine, Ms. Archer. Most of the time." He stepped inside and I was trapped between his bulk and my desk.

"Thanks, but I can always use improvement." I tried to toe the company line to secure my promotion and keep a smile on my face. But that was a mistake as he took my smile for a come-on. Maybe I reminded him of the naked dancing girls.

"Yes, you can, Diana," he breathed. He moved close, took me in his arms, and pushed me against the desk. He stank of gin.

My mind left the present and flashed back to a scene from a few months ago, not at all faded by time's passage.

✳

We'd had a software release party at the end of the workday and although there wasn't supposed to be liquor in the office, Mr. Dawl produced a bottle and persuaded us to have a drink with him. I knew I had to assemble the final technical manual after the party, but I accepted his proposal and he fixed mine himself.

An hour or so later when everyone else had gone, he came to my office and brought me another cocktail. Normally I didn't drink on an empty stomach, but fatigue had distorted my judgment.

We talked while I shuffled papers. He even helped me organize the pages. When we finished I went to the copy room. I loaded the thick manual into the feeder, started the machine to make multiple copies, and turned to the shelves. I wanted to be sure we had enough paper.

First I smelled gin, then two hands encircled and clutched me under my breasts. My initial reaction was panic. But Mr. Dawl's voice was soothing, "Don't be nervous, Diana. You're very beautiful and this is the right thing for us."

I didn't know what I could do, so I just stood there silently. And after a couple of moments his hands began to lift my breasts up and down.

"I thought they were real," he whispered. "Some bet they were, but others said you were…you know…enhanced."

I still said nothing. I'd seen men at the office stare at me and I'd thought it was because I was dressed nicely, but actually they'd been debating the reality of my bust. Then tears started. The boss had his hands on me, but I was more concerned about what others thought of my appearance.

After more intimate comments about my loveliness, he unbuttoned my blouse and his hands went inside and touched their way around. When his fingers slid under my bra, I let it happen.

When he heard my sigh of surrender, he growled and turned me around. As he did, the shelf onto which I'd been holding came off its brackets, collapsed, and dumped reams of paper onto the floor. There'd been stacks of multi-colored sheets along with the white so the resultant pile looked like a brilliantly dyed carpet. With minimal pressure he pushed me down onto this spread and then had his way, nearly mashing the life out of me.

In the midst, I thought I heard someone open the door, but I couldn't see. The copy machine continued to rhythmically crank out pages. Chunk, chunk, chunk…

When he finished, he sat back and looked at me sprawled in a heap on the floor. "That was terrific, but it's our secret." All I could do was nod. It was the darkest secret imaginable.

Then as he attempted to stand, he grabbed the copy machine cover in one hand, his pants in the other, and struggled. But the old machine couldn't take his tugging and its lid, which contained the rest of pages to be copied, broke loose. He stumbled backwards, lid still clutched in his left hand, and fanned paper from side to side across the room. Then with a splat, his bare, saggy ass landed on top of an unopened box of office supplies and squashed it.

"Damn!" he said as he looked at the cover in his hand. He threw it into the corner. The machine had stopped. "I wanted you to lie across the glass and make me a shot of your boobs for a souvenir, but, too bad, that'll have to wait until next time."

Next time! He'd just finished and he was already counting on a next time?

He staggered up with a satisfied grin, pulled up his pants, and, like a pseudo gentleman, stuck out his hand to help me up from the colored paper carpet. But as I pulled on it to stand, his scuffed wing-tip crushed my right foot.

"Thanks," he said with a little bow as I clung to the lidless machine, my clothes awry, my body already aching. "But mum's the word." Finger to his lips, he licked it. "And remember, if you don't like your job, Diana, there's a hundred more out there that'll take it in a heartbeat." He fixed his belt, straightened his tie, and left without a further word, shoelaces flapping. Blue-black tears rolled down my cheek and dripped, staining my new white bra.

I looked around and picked up my hose. I still had to finish making all the copies of the manual. I thought about going home, but what would I say to the others who were counting on me? It would be easier to finish, than to explain.

I blubbered, not very silently. My life stank. Then I collected the scattered pages, hobbled to another room, and restarted.

I left the colored paper mess on the floor right where it was.

Now here I was in my office with those snaky hands coming at me again. But this time I decided to resist. I didn't care about the consequences and my promotion could just be damned. I wasn't adding another sordid page to my sexual diary. Luckily I didn't have to. Someone yelled for Mr. Dawl. He had a call in the conference room. He let go and walked away in silence. The air around me expanded with a whoosh.

At first I was angry I'd let myself be trapped, but I knew it wasn't my fault. It was the boss who had the problem. I thought about harassment issues, but wasn't strong enough to deal with that.

Then the sick feeling from the Mr. Dawl's grope began to melt as I thought about Jon. He'd tell me not to tolerate anything that hurt my self-worth, but sometimes you can't help it. With my mother and grandmother gone, my father missing, and with no siblings or husband, there was only me, so I really needed that job and the smarmy boss was part of the punishment. I knew I deserved better, but didn't know how or where to find it.

Friday evening finally arrived and we were together. My heart was bathed in relief.

"I'm sorry I had to postpone our last workout," I said, starting the conversation as I pedaled. "Do you ever let clients go?"

"In here, when a client creates an unsafe situation by not following my instructions, I ask them to get another trainer. Outside, a person who only *wants to want to* improve takes my time from others who are serious."

"Wants to want to? What does that mean?"

"There are levels to desire. The first is *wanting*, the second is *wanting to want*, and the third is *wanting to want to want*. People in the third group have too much dust in their eyes so I refer them to other teachers."

"Dust in their eyes?"

"A person's inability to see and understand the true conditions of their life is what I call dust in their eyes."

"Do I have dust in my eyes?" I made eyes at Jon.

"A bit. But you recognize your life is not satisfactory and that you suffer. That has prompted you to change. You *want to* change. Not many can see that much. They work so hard and yet are so disillusioned. And they don't know what to do or where to look for relief."

"I understand," I said, "but sometimes my thoughts get mixed up."

"Don't be concerned. We'll untangle your mind's threads and then reweave them into a beautiful tapestry. But your warm-up is over and its time to exercise the pillars of your life, so let's start your stretches."

We went to the exercise room with the "X" painted on the glass door. I took out a mat. "Let's talk about truth," Jon said as I settled onto the floor.

Do I have a choice? But I'd become accustomed to the stream of information.

"Sure," I said as I stretched my hip, thigh, and calf muscles.

Other trainers talked to their clients during warm-ups, stretching, and rest periods. They talked about clubs, dating, music, sports, and television. But I was lucky. Mine talked to me about life.

Jon began, "First, you see there can be dissatisfaction in living."

"Yes, true."

"And you find that this dissatisfaction is caused by craving or attachment."

"That's true too."

"Next we see, in truth, there's a way to relieve this suffering by removing its cause. And lastly, we find this relief has steps."

"It does?"

"Yes," he said.

"The steps of this last truth fall into three groups," he continued. "The first group includes seeing and understanding how your life actually is and then developing the intention to go forward and make the changes needed to improve it. In the second group you learn to apply ethical behavior in your speech, your actions, your work, and in all your efforts. The third group involves quieting your mind chatter through mindfulness and concentration, that is, taming your monkey mind so you can be peaceful inside. The eight parts of these three groups act like the spokes of a wheel. And if all are strong your life rolls smoothly along."

True. And I wanted a smooth rolling life. I'd had enough jarring bumps caused by the wheel of my life being out of round, and enough of the wobbling caused by its being loose on its axle.

And as we left the room I realized I had learned truth in there.

"This is the Seated Leg Press," Jon said as we stepped into an area with machines that were new to me.

With my back flat against the seat and my feet on the plate, I released the carriage and pushed with my legs until I'd almost straightened them and then slowly let the weights down again. Next, as I lay on my stomach and tried not to think about my bottom poking up, I exercised my hamstring muscles on the Leg Curl machine. Then came Leg Extensions that exercised my quadriceps. And when I finished all those sets, I panted and sweated, and my legs glowed with heat. I had to stagger to the next machine.

"This is our last leg exercise," Jon said. He'd seated me at the Calf Raise machine and as I arched my feet up and down he explained that it made the calf muscles of my lower legs strong so I'd have a good gait.

"If you lack a balanced gait," he told me, "the movements of your body when you walk can cause mild to severe soreness in the hip, knee, and ankle joints, and you want to avoid that."

When I finally finished and drank from my water bottle, he said, "If you put in this much energy each time we workout, soon your legs will be big and strong."

It took a moment for his words to sink in. Big muscular legs? No! I wanted slender, dancer's legs.

"But I don't want big thick legs," I said with worried concern. "I'd also end up with a big thick bottom." I envisioned Oscar and some of the women I'd seen in fitness magazines.

"Sorry, I didn't mean it that way. The difference is between building and toning. Building means causing muscles to grow. And toning means improving the quality of the muscles you have. The program I've planned will do both, but with emphasis on toning. You'll become fit and trim, and that's your goal, isn't it?"

"Well...yes," I answered. But I'd also seen myself as a gorgeous Superwoman whacking bosses and ripping off car doors with only a twitch of my finger.

"Okay, you're rested," he said. "Now follow me."

"I thought we were only doing legs?"

"Every now and then I like to throw in a surprise. You'll like it." I doubted that.

We went to a bench hinged in the middle and as I lay on my back I reached up and gripped two handles next to my ears.

"Lift only your torso by bending at the waist," he instructed. "Try to pull your ribs to your thighs. This exercise strengthens and tones your abdominal muscles. I want you to add it to every workout."

"Wow, I'm so lucky."

As I crunched up and down, my stomach growled and my belly shook as the muscles worked, and although I didn't look like Santa, there was more in my middle than I wanted.

Then at last I was done and Jon looked satisfied.

"Two other things, then you can stretch and bike," he said.

"No other exercise machines! Please!"

"No. Only a couple of comments. First, remember as your muscle strength increases, your mental strength increases. Then it's easier to resist unpleasant things entering your life. And second, I'm glad you ditched your baggy clothes, Diana. I'm sure you're more comfortable and you look much better."

"They were hard to let go of," I said as I warmed to his compliment. "I was safe, all wrapped up. I stood out, but felt hidden."

"I know you did," Jon said, "but now you don't need to do that anymore."

# Chapter Eight: Shower Visions

*"You will have obstacles and you must pass them, but you will see they are hollow, empty, and you will realize that it is all just appearances."*

"*It's* always something!" I exclaimed, exasperated, looking around for someone to blame. A drop of sweat splashed on the window and split my flushed, suffering reflection with its salty streak.

When I'd returned late from lunch, the lot was full and I'd had to park so far from the building I'd almost needed binoculars to see it. And then after work and after I'd hiked in my work heels all the way across its black, broiling and potholed surface, I tore my new dress and scraped my hose and thigh on a sharp piece of metal sticking out from the junker parked beside my car.

But my ordeal wasn't over. As I stood in the afternoon sun, I burned and throbbed, and I discovered my car keys were still in my office. In my stealthy escape they'd been forgotten.

Earlier while at lunch I'd left a throw-down purse on my desk as a decoy so my real purse with my spare set of keys was locked in the car's trunk. I wanted to scream! I cursed and blamed everyone. Why was I the one always punished? It was their fault not mine. But as usual, I was wrong…and I was melting.

Mr. Dawl caught me as I snuck back out with my recovered keys.

"Off to see your trainer *boy*, Ms. Archer?" he sneered, drink in hand.

"Well…yes. I have a workout at seven," I said. I tried not to smile in anticipation.

"You can go after one drink and a couple of sandwiches," he said and pointed one in my face. It was putrid. "I insist."

I saw no escape and still thought I had a career to protect. "All right."

"Good. Now come join the group." He followed me closely as I made my way to the conference room.

This was what I'd tried to avoid. All week I'd known there was an office party planned for late Friday afternoon and I'd wanted no part of it. But now I went, had my Dawl-made drink, and listened to him tell stupid jokes.

As we ate the tasteless treats, he asked, "Do you know why you shouldn't take food to the beach?"

No one knew. Or they wouldn't speak up.

"Because of the sand which is there!" he guffawed loudly and slapped his leg.

Manager wanna-be's howled with laughter, the others smiled and looked away. I belched into the ruckus. The boss's chins and his bowl full of jelly shook vigorously.

One thing I hadn't counted on, however, was seeing Mr. Dawl chase after Tina, a temp who hoped for a permanent position. I'd heard a rumor, but I hadn't expected him to be so blatant, especially in front of me. And as I watched them coo together it had a strange effect. I was jealous. Maybe that was his plan. It sounded crazy because although I didn't want him pursuing me, I didn't want him after anyone else. It must be the liquor.

When they disappeared down the hall in the direction of the copy room, I made my excuses and left, keys in hand.

By the time I got to my car the streets were as stuffed as a tick and I understood what the Aussies meant when they said, "Bloody hell!" I called Four Palms, said I'd be late, but I'd be there, sometime...

Screeching tires announced my arrival as I tried to drive and fix my lipstick. As my heart pounded and tire rubber stank, I recalled my previous accident, but this time I envisioned myself flying through the windshield into the bed of the nasty truck in front of me and smashing my newly whitened teeth on its dented toolbox. That would have been bloody hell for sure. Luckily, I was spared and I went straight to Jon's office.

"You look worn out," he said as I dropped into a chair.

I nodded. The near impact combined with the strong drink and spoiled sandwiches had made me queasy.

"I'd like to suggest an alternative for this evening," he said. "You worked hard this past Monday and Wednesday, so tonight why don't you bike for thirty minutes. Then take a hot shower. And when you finish, let's have dinner. We can workout tomorrow—on Saturday."

I don't know what I expected Jon to say, but that wasn't it. I allowed his words sink in. I was going from coffee girl to dinner girl! I couldn't think any further.

"I don't have my shower shoes," I finally blurted. Engage your mind before you speak, I reminded myself, again.

Jon laughed. "I'll loan you mine."

He went to his gym bag, pulled out a pair of dark blue shower shoes with brown soles, put them into a clear plastic bag, and handed it to me.

"Come back when you're ready and we'll go. I'll do paperwork until then."

"You're going to be here tomorrow?" I'd recovered from my shocks and I couldn't believe he'd come in on his day off just for me.

"I'll be here. You'll get your workout so please don't be concerned."

"It isn't the workout. It's your time. You don't come in on Saturdays."

"I do tomorrow, for you. Now go bike, I'm hungry."

As I left, Jon called, "Level One!"

While changing in the locker room, I noticed I had a long smear of purplish-red lipstick that trailed upward from the left corner of my mouth and ended mid-cheek.

After a twenty-five-minute bike ride, I was relaxed. The week's events had been dripped onto the floor where they evaporated into insignificance. As I finished, I anticipated my shower.

The second time I'd come to the gym there had been two women playing, "Mirror, mirror, on the wall." Tonight they sat on the bench in front of my favorite locker, No. 55.

I'd selected this locker because five plus five equals ten. Once, after a couple of glasses of wine, Andrea and I had called a psychic hot line. The woman who answered told me my lucky number was ten and wherever I encountered this number, I would be fortunate.

These women, however, were in my way. Undeterred, I pushed past them and opened *my* locker.

"Let's ask her," the lighter blond woman said.

"See this mole on my face." She leaned closer and pointed to a black spot on her left temple. "Do you think it's a beauty mark like famous women have?"

"How long have you had it?" I asked, surprised at her question.

"It's been growing for a few months. Some days I like it, other days I don't."

"I'd have it checked," I said. "It might be something dangerous from too much sun."

"Well, I go to the beach a lot, but I use sunscreen. A dark tan makes your body look hot and men like that, if you know what I mean."

I knew what she meant, but by the way she looked at me, she probably thought it was a foreign experience.

"I'd get it checked anyway," I persisted.

"And you be sure she does," I said to her friend.

They both looked surprised, but they nodded.

"I'll go and while I'm there I can find out about the new skin treatments," the lighter blond said. "There are so many of them now."

Then as I turned to my locker, the jitters began. Undressing around women I always felt like I was being judged, so I decided I was not going to disrobe in front of this fit pair of blondes.

I gathered my raspberry bath gel, a loofa, and Jon's shower shoes, and then walked fully clothed into a shower stall. Its frosted glass door gave me the illusion of privacy. I undressed, hung my clothes over the door, and turned on the water to an anxiety-soothing temperature. Then I remembered his shower shoes. I dumped them from the bag, rinsed them, and put them on my feet. As the welcoming warm water washed over me, my skin softened and my stress-stuffed pores smiled.

For a minute or so the shower embraced me and then...I was somewhere else.

When you dream, a part of you knows you are dreaming. Even so, you go with the flow of the story because of its seeming reality.

But when I think back to that shower experience, maybe it wasn't a dream at all.

I stood among silver-white trees whose yellow and green leaves chatted with barely overheard conversation. Clad in rough, tan garments trimmed in dark blue, I wore no underclothes and the rough fabric prickled. I closed my eyes.

I became a woodland wanderer and crept through forested valleys studded with boulders scattered in a labyrinth, their days of basking in the sunlight barely remembered. All around me, bushes and trees stretched and shouted, while ferns and mosses, coating the ground at the feet of their loud relatives, sang with the stream as it flowed from beneath the earth.

In a clearing, bears stood and conversed around a log fire. While above me, birds carried touristy news from one locale to another. Other animals communicated among themselves with only a look or a glance, each fraught with intent, and sought nothing more than to be secure in ways only they could understand.

And as this panorama unfolded before me, I was one with all and knew that if all would help the one, what a beautiful balance there would be.

My eyes started open. The breeze had shifted and my coarse garments couldn't warm its crispness. And there was a dense scent, unidentifiable yet familiar, so I faced into the wind and walked as gusts of smell rose and fell in strength. I was compelled to find its source.

At first, the ground had only a slight uphill grade. The steepness increased until I was crawling, angling between stones and trees, swimming in twigs and leaves. My hands, knees, and stomach became green from crushed moss as I wriggled through the thickening scent. Its call colored my exhilaration with unease.

Pulling myself upward using roots and rocks, I finally pushed between the knotty trunk of a forest monarch and a huge granite boulder upon whose pitted face grey lichens and pink feldspar crystals vied for dominance. Mid-gap, I stood and then bent and straightened my knees several times and sensuously scratched both sides of my body. Then I squeezed through the narrow slice, dropped back to the ground, and looked about cat-like.

I saw a small plain partially encircled by sheer cliffs. Behind me, the sunlight trickled through the trees and its hues shifted as though prismed through jewels. And atop the tall enclosing rock walls, the spiky crests sparkled. The vale had its own tiara!

I looked deeper and saw in the far curve of the canyon a craggy-mouthed grotto between two large trees. This was the source of the scent. I was apprehensive as I stood and walked to it.

When I arrived at the wide threshold, I saw deep gouges in the rock over the opening and as the sunlight winked, they spelled a word: Friend.

"Come in, Friend." A booming voice shook my ears, rattled my consciousness. "I welcome you with love."

As the echoes faded, the veil dropped from my eyes and mind, and I entered along a path worn into a floor clean of leaves as a fox walked past unafraid and departed.

I was in a tall rectangular hall. Large tapestries hung on the walls and depicted indiscernible scenes that seemed to shift and change.

Where the rock was exposed, thousands of inch-long quartz crystals reflected the sunset pouring in through the doorway by shooting thin beams of light. Dust in the air made the white rays seem almost solid.

Across the rear wall of the chamber, diagonal crystalline veins cut from ceiling to floor. The visual pressure that radiated from their purple, white, and shiny black minerals made them appear as glowing ribbons lit from behind.

Then as the late afternoon sun slowly released its power to the night, the glittery veins and the room-shooting beams darkened. And as they did, red urns began sending out firefly-colored light from their throats and I could see more details.

To my left were four ornate wooden cabinets, a dining table with two carved chairs, and three taller cabinets. Glowing urns rested on the cabinets and one was on the table. And sitting at the table was a man, the source of the voice.

His deep red garments blended into the dark wood and medium words applied: medium height and weight, medium colored hair and skin, and medium aged. With a long-fingered hand, he beckoned me to come closer.

"Welcome, Bold Traveler!" he said, and a surge of acceptance filled me. The pitch was deep, the intonation exact. The voice was the embodiment of everything good that had ever come before. His smile radiated from his eyes, his cheeks, his mouth, but I found it wasn't easy to concentrate when I looked at his face. Then as I moved closer to him, his energy enveloped me and a liquid image came into my mind.

I was immersed in a huge copper vat of warm and oh-so-loving chocolate. Smooth succulent chocolate covered me. It softened and melted me. And as I lifted my hands over my head, its liquid creaminess slid over my skin. It dripped from my face and ears; it tickled my breasts. It was between my fingers, between my toes and legs, and in my hair. Its taste fondled my tongue. The feeling was like when my trainer was near… And as the fantasy ended, it was hard to return to where I was.

The chair he offered me was worn and warm; it's padded seat was covered with hazelnut shells and hair. I brushed them aside and sat. But before… Thunk…Thunk! I jumped! The table shook. I shook! The strange man had cracked another nut. He pushed its fragments toward me. I tried to be polite as I picked through the debris, but what an odd thing this was to be doing after my hard climb.

"Would you like tea?"

"Yes, please."

He produced an earthenware mug and poured tea from a brown pot with an intricate handle.

"Perhaps a bit of bread and jelly?"

I accepted his hospitality without any further thought.

"What have you brought me?"

I was surprised by his question and felt compelled to comply as any good guest would, but I hadn't come prepared. I checked my clothes, but all I could find was an empty snail shell I'd picked up in the forest. I held it up.

He accepted it graciously as if what I'd offered him was a treasure and carefully placed it on a shelf among other curious objects.

Then we chatted about trivial things like the forest beings and his laundry while we dined on nuts, raspberry tea, kumquat jelly, and brown bread. When we finished, he wiped his sticky fingers on a blue cloth and picked at his teeth with the sharp edge of a nutshell.

Our stomachs were full and I became sleepy. As he moved to a square platform in the middle of the room, he told me to be comfortable on the numerous pillows that surrounded it. I went to them and was enveloped by silken splendor. My mind went ahhhh.

Along the wall to my right was a desk with an elegant high-backed chair. On the desk were piles of paper weighted with smooth, inscribed stones. Writing instruments from every age stood alert in circular red and black vases.

Stacks of books, some made from narrow strips of wood and others inscribed in clay, formed small hills around which lay scrolls tied with bright cloth or belted with silver.

Other unidentifiable things as well as the ordinary were littered among the books: pieces of pottery, feathers, and a box with a smiling moon painted on its lid. Cradled in her crescent was a long-eared animal.

A raised sleeping area in the back corner had thick brown bedding and plump fern-green pillows. On the wall over the bed hung a plaque, partially obscured by the shadows, with a fancy wheel, a flower, and other unseen designs carved into its surface.

The compelling scent had finally faded away, and everything here was soft and cozy. I rested.

Minutes or hours had passed when the man on the platform suddenly cleared his throat with an, "Ahummm."

"Wake up, Diana! You have questions. Questions you wish to have answered."

And although his voice was in front of me, it was also an inch from my ears—both ears. I sat up on the cushions and listened.

"You have chosen to follow a different path. And you will not turn aside.

"You see that everything is conditioned, everything is made of parts, and you know that as these parts arise and cease, everything arises and ceases."

His voice deepened and increased in volume. It was ringing in my head. I held my brow.

"With your body and senses you contact the world. You develop feelings, thirsts, and attachments to pleasures, opinions, trivialities. This clinging brings you dissatisfaction, and release from its pain requires awareness—and letting go."

With his words, the two largest urns on either side of the platform began to send out reddish-yellow light full of white sparks. I covered my face and looked out between my fingers.

"A new understanding of life is dawning within you. Through perception, concentration, and absorption of its meaning you see that the law of existence is four-fold: loving-kindness, compassion, joy, and equanimity.

"Those four become five to live by: kindness, generosity, truthfulness, mindfulness, and contentment.

"Are you listening, Diana?"

"Yes—yes!" I rolled onto my side and watched through squinted eyes. I held my head with both hands. His voice boomed and the ground quivered.

"As you increase these five your wisdom develops. Your mind is a mirror reflecting all things without attachment, both in their uniqueness and in their unity. You see similarities and differences, but with no distinction and no discrimination. The sun of your mind shines evenly on all. The mirror of your mind reflects everything that exists and nothing sticks."

And as I began to understand the compassion in his voice and words, the volume decreased and the thunder softened slightly.

"From this, blossom. Live freely, naturally, and spontaneously. Choose your choices. And as the whole of space is filled by the sun's rays, the whole of life is filled by happiness.

"Then from the flowering of your wisdom comes the skillful means of helping others. Assist them in making selections that remove the sources of their unhappiness. Help them to grow and to bloom.

"To get here you followed the scent of relief, relief from your fears and from your sorrows. You were compelled to find truth.

"You will have obstacles and you must pass them, but when you look back, you will see they are hollow, empty, and you will realize that it is all just appearances. And remember, teachings are but a raft.

"Lastly, at the bottom of all things, beyond the fears and the sufferings are only two: gratitude and service.

"Happiness is your journey and your destination. Maintain it even during turbulence. And don't go back to sleep."

My ears were full. I couldn't listen anymore. His voice dropped in pitch and slowed. He raised his hand and pointed at me.

"I will give you a gift, Diana. *Lean back, and hold onto nothing.*"

Then his voice stopped and a surge of sun-bright color erupted. The lights dazzled and white pinpoints jetted from the two urns. I heard a rushing sound and the rattle of objects on the shelves. I shut my eyes.

For a second nothing happened, and then the pain swiftly grew. It grew and burst! And with its detonation, all the fears, hurts, angers, resentments, bad experiences, unskillful choices, lies, and dissatisfactions I'd ever had or caused others to have, erupted in a titanic explosion that blew my consciousness apart. A wail of terror and release from all the suffering I'd ever known tore from my mouth. My flaming body arched and twisted, shook and collapsed. My bladder filled to bursting and then let go a streaming acid geyser that gushed out like liquid fire frying my thighs and legs. Pain poured from every pore. I passed out.

Warm liquid ran over my face. I slowly opened my eyes and found that I lay nude, limbs askew, in shadows on the tile floor of the shower, the water streaming down. I turned my head and saw in the grainy light from the frosted shower door that my bra and underwear blocked the drain. Jon's shoes, the loofa, and my hair were afloat. The water level hadn't risen above the doorsill, so I was bathing in a shallow, rippling pool of warm water and hot urine. And the smell was a horrible stinking vapor permeated with the excrement of mind and body. Fear and loathing must smell like this when released into the world, I thought. Yet I realized I was clean inside, but splashing in a lifetime of anguish and free-floating anxieties. Shaky, I sat up, and then with a quick toe thrust, I kicked the clothes away from the drain.

When I'd returned from wherever I'd been, I stood and scrubbed until the skin everywhere I could reach was red. I thought about getting someone to wash my back, but they might not understand. I rubbed it against the stall's walls.

When I finished, I opened the door and peeped. There was no one in the shower room, but I could hear voices in the locker area. The agonized cry from my experience must not have been heard in this reality. No one had come running; no one had called the club management. Why the stall light had burned out, I had no clue.

I turned off the water and then discovered I'd left my towel in my locker. My shirt and shorts had fallen into the putrid pool, which also filled my cross-training shoes. I stared at them and my situation with equanimity. There was only one solution.

I picked up the soggy pile, threw the whole load into the trash, and then washed my hands. As I shook them dry, I walked naked into the locker area and to my lucky locker.

The stares scorched and the conversations dried up fast. I looked a mess: out of shape, hair full of rats, eyes puffy, scratches on my stomach, and glowing red skin, but there was no smell. None.

The two blondes hurried away, but their presence told me only minutes had passed while I was in the shower. My old watch, in the pocket of my shorts, had also met its demise. I opened my locker, took out my towel, and began to dry my hair. I was oblivious to everyone.

While I toweled the rest of my body, Sarah, the blonde trainer, dashed into the locker room and came to a shoe-screeching stop. She stared. Her teeth gaped.

"Yes?" I asked mildly.

"Ah...uh...Jon asked me to check on you. He thought you might be...uh...in distress." She mouthed the words with puffs. I almost felt sorry for her.

"I'm fine. I had a delay, but tell him I'll be right along. Thanks." I continued to dry my reddened body.

"Uh...right! You got it!" And with a squeaky spin, Sarah departed.

I took out my dark green jeans, a blue and white sweater top, my work shoes, and got dressed, sans underwear. I paid no attention to the others who watched cautiously, their conversations resuming.

Then I went to the shower room and into the shadowy stall. I picked up his shoes, washed them, and put them into my bag.

Our dinner tonight would be my treat.

# Chapter Nine: Dining in the Dark

*"What's amazing about the secrets of the Universe is...they aren't secret."*

*Boooom!* The thunder rattled the car windows a split-second after the lightning illuminated the Valencia's door. As I ducked the streetlights flickered. I released my seatbelt and waited for the rain to slow. I knew I was going to have to make a run for it.

The forecaster had predicted thunderstorms as the worst thing that could happen. But I enjoyed them. In Tampa we were used to lots of storms every year—big ones. The lightning and thunder cleared the air of man-made distractions, and the wind and rain swept the air clean of man-made emotions. Afterwards I always felt renewed.

As the downpour paused, I got out and walked toward the restaurant. A truck drove past, its tires squishing on the pavement. The driver's profile looked unhappy. Not me! I was spontaneous and clean! And I wanted to share it! The rain restarted with wide-apart drops and as I neared the building, the drops got closer together.

They were cold! They had started as pinpoints from somewhere on high and then grew as they fell. How fortunate for the ones that touched my skin. They experienced the ecstatic change from an icy-hearted drop to one warmed by the loving fires of a living being. I could almost feel the thrill of their bursts.

Some twenty feet from the entrance, I stopped. The storm had freshened, but I didn't care. And then I twirled around and around. I closed my eyes and put out my arms. I turned faster and faster. Raindrops flew.

As I spun, my thoughts beamed out—thoughts of love and kinship for beings great and small, thoughts of peace of mind and contentment for everyone, thoughts of ending all forms of suffering. I was a powerful lighthouse of love and light to guide those who journeyed in the dark to safety and serenity.

Then as my whirling slowed, my melodious dance ended, but I didn't feel dizzy. And when I opened my eyes I was facing the restaurant. Inside the half-curtained window two people watched, Jon and another man. A sudden flash of lightning lit my finale, and to its rapid-fire thunderclap, I hurried in through the door.

"Good evening and welcome," the tall, deep-voiced host said.

I was embarrassed about my performance. But he handed me a small towel and I dried my face and fluffed my hair by the light of candles in hurricane lamps.

"You must be hungry after your beautiful dance," he said as he led the way. And as Jon followed me, I could feel his eyes.

The table was at the back and it was a booth. I sat down facing the wall.

"Not on that side," our host said. "The lady always sits where she has the best view."

Then after I resettled, he continued, "I'm pleased to greet you on this night of weather. I'll send over my best waiter: my son. You will not lack for anything, my friends." A short bow and he was gone.

"Slide over," Jon said. Then he pushed the booth's seat and me nearer to the table.

He was much stronger than he looked!

"Kick off your shoes and put your feet on the seat across from you. That way you can relax and enjoy dinner. You've had a big day! You need nourishment."

I stretched out my tired legs as Jon sat next to me. Yes! I said silent thanks. Heat and strength pulsed off of him and his proximity grounded me. I was safe, warm and dry, and about to be fed. All was right with my world.

The waiter materialized dressed in a starched white shirt. One second the air was empty, the next he was there. He nodded to Jon, who ordered sparkling water with slices of lime and orange, and appetizers. The waiter vanished.

"I know you had something happen," Jon said. He glanced over at me.

"How do you know that?" But I wasn't surprised.

"We won't talk about it now, but when a person experiences something mystical their first reaction is to try to get a quick explanation in everyday terms. But there may not be one. So let it be. Its purpose will become clear."

"Do you know what happened?"

"Not exactly, and it's not the last."

"Not the last! What else is coming?" I tried not to show apprehension.

"We'll wait and see. But even if I knew what to expect, I wouldn't say because I don't know your highest good."

"But I'd feel better if I knew that everything will be all right in the end."

"Where the 'end' is, I don't know, but I am certain you'll be a different person before long and you'll cherish and respect that person. And then all the good things you want from your life will come. I guarantee it."

"You guarantee it?"

"Sure. Want to shake?"

I laughed aloud. "No, I trust you."

"You have a beautiful laugh, especially when it's genuine."

"You've changed the subject!"

"Of course. The black bean fritters and plantain chips are here."

While we ate, he asked what I wanted for my main course.

"What do you recommend?"

"Let me pick something for you—something delicious."

I hesitated. This would take courage on my part. Relatives and former boyfriends had given me what they thought *I deserved,* and not what *I wanted or needed.* I wondered if I could trust him. I wanted our dinner to be special.

"Okay," I said as I took a leap of faith. "Do you do this for all your dates?"

"No. What I've usually found is that they like to select what they want, but then prefer me to order."

"You don't mind?"

"Not at all."

And then when Jon ordered for me, I noticed two women elbow their dates and heard one of them whisper, "Why don't you ever do that?"

Later, his platter of seafood paella over saffron rice smelled as good as my citrus shrimp kabobs. We filled our stomachs. His didn't bulge like mine, but no underwear or pantyhose relieved me of any excess pressure.

Finally, we sat back and decided the rest had to go with us.

"Would you like dessert?" The waiter had appeared again. "We have warm flan or fresh rum cake."

"No, I'm full. Thanks," Jon said. "And I don't eat much sugar."

"Neither do I," I quickly added. You'd have to define much.

Then, the lights went out.

✳

Dinner had been so peaceful that only an occasional rumble of thunder had registered and I'd almost forgotten about the weather. Some people exited the restaurant and entered the tempest.

"Let's sit and talk," Jon said. "The storm will pass."

I wanted it to last all night.

Then the owner came over with a fat white candle inside an etched-glass lantern.

"Perhaps some decaf coffee, please," Jon requested.

"My son will be right over," the owner answered, and then went and hung the bright lantern in the front window.

"He seems happy you're here," I said.

"I enjoy his company too. And when he says, 'It's good to see you!' he truly means it."

But I wanted to know more about Jon.

"At Four Palms they say no one knows anything about you."

"That's not really true, however I do have something I should explain." He drew in a deep breath.

"People say they want to know you, but many times what they really mean is show me your wounds, your weaknesses, and I'll show you mine. Or they mean if I show you my wounds, even if you don't ask, then you have to show me yours whether you want to or not. There are variations, but those two statements capture the essence. It's an equation and both sides have to be equal. I call it playing woundology."

"What's...that?" The turn of his conversation had jolted me.

"They're not physical wounds," Jon said without noticing my surprise, "although a man once showed me a hideous gash on his thigh that had been oozing for years. It was the basis of his life and he'd display it without request and without warning."

When I'd asked Jon to talk about himself, this wasn't what I'd expected to hear. For after-dinner conversation it wasn't very pleasant. He continued less graphically.

"The wounds I'm talking about are mental ones, the ones people use as excuses for their unhappiness. And true, some wounds are beyond our control, but many are of our own making.

"People make unskillful choices which lead to unpleasant problems. Then they trot out the consequences of those poor decisions and they expect you to commiserate. Poor pitiful me, they say. Some even take it to the level of a verbal competitive sport with the volleys going back and forth until a winner is declared—the one with the most wounds. It's ironic, the least happy person wins. In groups there'll be a pecking order of wounding and any person that joins must display theirs in order to fit in. Through this dynamic, any organization can end up in a hierarchy with the unhappiest person at the top. From outside you can't see this, but if you're inside, you know."

This still wasn't the sort of reflection I wanted after a big meal. But then I thought of the opportunities I'd passed by when I didn't have the courage to do what I knew was right for me. The sad part was I did it to please someone I thought had my best interests in mind. But Jon's words had made me realize that the other person's good intentions were many times only extensions of their own misfortunes and fears. And when they convinced me not to grow in my most beneficial direction, they protected themselves from having to look at their own poor choices.

"Sorry," he said. "I know that's not the best coffee conversation, but I wanted you to have some background. People don't know me because I won't play woundology."

"Have you explained that to them?"

"Most aren't interested. And when their need to play is frustrated, they get away from me fast. Games like that have only one purpose—to increase misery."

"So why do people play them?"

"Because the 'winner' receives a tiny bit of power over the 'loser.' And from this, a tiny bit of pleasure is generated. But because these bits are so fleeting, like a camera flash, the game has to be repeated, endlessly. I won't waste my energy on it anymore."

"Thank you for telling me about that," I said, grateful I'd listened. "I wish I'd been smart enough to discover it sooner."

"Well, even intelligent people have things about which they're ignorant, and by ignorant I only mean unaware. And that also includes me. But one day you'll find everything I've passed on to you, you've known all along. What's amazing about the secrets of the Universe is…they aren't secret. We're just too hasty to see them."

"I've never been any good at discovering secrets."

"When you come from a place of quiet," Jon said, "you'll be able to pierce any veil. And tomorrow after we workout, I'll give you something more to think about."

"Please tell me now." I wanted a sweet nothing.

"All right." He smiled. "Before you take any action, ask yourself, 'Will this bring peace into my life, or will it lessen the peace I already have?'"

"That's it?" Not what I wanted.

"That's it. And you'll find the more you remember this, the easier your life will be."

The overhead lights flickered making his eyes look mysterious.

"Will you answer a few questions for me?" I asked as the room went dark again. "You can elaborate if you'd like, but please give me answers I can understand."

"Okay. I apologize for being wordy, but I have a lot to share. And I don't know how much time we'll have, so I let the thoughts flow. I don't mean to overwhelm you."

Didn't know how much time we might have? BPM had mentioned that. My thoughts went frantic and my other questions flew away. And although I usually didn't ask men out, I looked down at my lap and swallowed.

"Instead of working out tomorrow, would you like to drive to Lettuce Lake? We could walk, and maybe have something to eat on the way back." I put hope in my voice. His pause lasted longer than I wished.

"I'm sorry. I have a commitment I must keep." And after a rain-filled silence, he said, "You have more questions?"

"They might be personal."

"That's all right."

"Are you seeing anyone special?" I'd embarrassed myself, so why not get it all out?

"No. Not right now."

"Why not now?" I was blunt, and tired.

"Because there are two things I require in a relationship: loving-kindness and compassion."

"Is that all?"

"Unless you want more explanation."

"Please."

"For me the two most important qualities needed in a relationship are loving-kindness and compassion. Ironically, few men or women possess enough in their own lives—look how they treat themselves—to have any left to share with another. It's difficult to give true loving-kindness and compassion, if you don't have enough for yourself."

He continued, "Loving-kindness is unlimited friendliness. It's a practice of the heart. But due to busyness and superficiality, most people have no knowledge of heart. They hear the word and have a vague notion about being good or kind. But stresses, many self-chosen, have driven friction between our hearts and minds.

"The *heart* is that part of you that knows right from wrong, what's skillful and unskillful. It can distinguish between these distinctly.

There are no shades of gray. Shades of gray only arise when the heart says unskillful, but the mind wants it anyway.

"We are born with this knowing heart. Culture gives us overlays to justify its own behavior, but in that quiet place within, right before sleep or right after we awaken, we know the truth, both about ourselves and about our world. When we proceed from a place of right, we know it, and when we proceed from a place of wrong, we also know it. These are our gut feelings and intuition. And they are why people fear aloneness.

"So, what do I mean by skillful behavior, which is also known as right behavior? Skillful behaviors are those words or actions that increase peace and happiness in ourselves and in those around us. If any word or deed, and that includes thoughts, decreases our own peace and happiness, or the peace and happiness of anyone else, it is unskillful. Cultivating skillful behavior yields a bountiful life harvest. Unskillful behavior yields a bitter crop that poisons and doesn't nurture.

"And so how do you use this in your life and relationships? The answer is to choose kindness instead of rightness. *Choose kindness over rightness.* Sounds simple, but putting this tool for harmonious living into practice in our hurry-up world requires alertness and awareness—awareness of what you know and awareness of how your words, actions, and thoughts affect others.

"Sometimes pain can come from choosing kindness. But instead of blaming, become more kind. Don't waste your moments on bitterness or resentment.

"Now let's tie these ideas back to the heart. If I have skillful thoughts, skillful words and actions will flow from them and I am living from my heart. My reward is a happy and secure life. Loving-kindness permeates my world. But if I insist on having unskillful thoughts, unskillful actions will result and I am not living from my heart. I am out of alignment both with myself and with my world. My reward is friction, dissatisfaction, and sadness, and I'm submerged in continuous fear, guilt, and worry.

"And finally to answer your question, I'm careful with whom I have a relationship because I want loving-kindness to be the norm, the day-to-day power. But it's difficult to find a person who wants to approach a relationship from a place of tranquility and harmony, the place where the love and light of union originate."

As he said "love and light," the ceiling bulbs lit, and stayed on.

I'd lost track of where I was, but as the waiter came over I saw we were the only people remaining.

"Please bring me the check," I requested.

"Madam, there is no check."

For a moment I was confused, no check and being called Madam. My mother and grandmother had been "Madam."

"Why not?" Fatigue had crept in and I didn't want to play games.

"There's never a check when he comes in," he answered, indicating Jon.

There was nothing else to be said. The waiter left.

"I'll tell you about compassion another time. At the lake or the beach."

"I'd love that." I'd forgotten about compassion, and the lake. The beach?

"Time to go home, Diana," Jon said as he rose. He towered above me. Then he leaned over, blew out the candle, and offered me his hand.

# Chapter Ten: Saturday's Stomach

*"The hardest part about going to the gym is going to the gym."*

*It* was 11:17 a.m., Saturday.

"Arise and shine, sweetheart," Jon whispered.

He had interrupted a wonderful dream. People liked me. I was important and loved. The memories spilled away. Sweetheart?

Under damp skies the night before we'd agreed to workout at eleven which had seemed reasonable at the time. Now I would be more than an hour late.

"We can cancel if you want."

I loved to hear Jon's voice in my ear while I was in bed.

"No, I'll be right there. It won't take long."

Since Mr. Cheaters, my orange and white tabby with one chewed ear, had run off after being kicked by a jealous boyfriend, there was only me. I splashed my face with cold water, dug in my dresser for a clean tee shirt and shorts, and dressed, with underwear. I located my old athletic shoes in the dust bunnies under the bed and I rummaged through the books and unopened mail on the dresser top to find my keys.

✳

"Drop your things in a locker and do a 10-minute warm-up. It's ab day," Jon said when I walked in.

After I stowed my bag, I went to the shower stall and cautiously looked inside. I thought I heard the faint rustle of leaves. "Was it only last night?" I sighed aloud. "It was so real!"

"Since I know you like to read, Diana, I've brought you a list of helpful books. These are ones you can review at your leisure," Jon said as I finished on the treadmill.

"Thanks." But I still had to ask, "Last night you said something about there wasn't much time. Are you leaving?"

"Don't worry, I haven't decided yet and when I do you'll be the first to know. But let me explain. Four Palms likes aggressive sales people and that isn't my path. If someone doesn't want to buy, I don't push because it only increases their dissatisfaction.

"Four Palms also wants me to take on more clients, but I like to have fewer so I can devote quality time to each. I believe in work first, and then play, but I also have to have time for fun. Many times, no play has made me numb to my life. And I don't want to be someone whose bliss is covered by a heavy load of work and caged by thick bars of debt. My life is too valuable to pass that way.

"So I'm not certain what will happen. And that's all right. If life's adventures were planned, they wouldn't be adventures, they'd be work.

"I might spend time with my teachers," he ended.

"Doesn't not knowing worry you?" I asked in disbelief. But it was not knowing about us that was my real worry. Why couldn't being together with me be more important to someone than anything else?

"If it's something I can change, I do, and I don't worry," he said, without seeming to notice my feelings. "And if it's something I can't change, worry won't help, so I let it go."

Although I was very unhappy, I didn't want him to see it so I changed the subject. "You mentioned teachers?"

"I'm from a lineage of teachers and because I can't know everything no matter how hard I try, seeing my teachers helps keep me focused."

"Then Jon that's what I want to call you too—my teacher," I said. "Because that's what you do, you teach me."

"All right." He seemed a little surprised by my statement. "Teacher is fine. It's what I call myself. Now let's do your stretches," he said, as he held open the door to the "X" room.

"Lie supine on the Ab Bench, please." We had left the "X" room and arrived at the first exercise machine.

I must have looked confused because he said, "Sorry. Supine means on your back. When you're prone, you're lying on your stomach."

"You learn something new every day," I said.

I lay on the bench, placed my feet on the footrests, and grasped the handles. To a slow count of three, I bent at my waist and lifted my upper body. I paused for a moment at the top and then lowered.

During the rests between sets he explained the importance of having proper abdominal strength. This was a version of the strong stomach theme I hadn't heard.

"It's very important," he began, "to have strong abdominal muscles because your body depends on them for balance, for bending and rotating, and for the compression required for deep breathing. But for most people they are the most neglected set of muscles in the body. The benefits of a strong, flexible mid-section are numerous and the much sought-after six-pack stomach is just an extra reward."

There were no long pauses today. When I rested between sets it gave my muscles time to rebuild their adenosine triphosphate, or ATP, and the dialogue between us kept my thoughts off exercise. I had learned the mind was not always your friend when it came to health issues and to overcome its resistance to change was hard. It required a sustained effort. As Jon observed, "The hardest part about going to the gym is going to the gym."

"Now let's do Leg Lifts," he said. "You're face up again on this bench with your head toward the raised end. Reach up over your head and grab these handles for balance."

I kept my head aligned with my spine, my feet together, and my legs straight as I slowly lifted my legs upward as far as I could, pivoting at the hip. Then I paused for a moment and slowly lowered them.

"Remember to breathe out as you raise your legs and breathe in as you lower them," Jon coached.

After the Leg Lifts it was difficult to walk to the Seated Ab Crunch machine. And when I finally finished my sets there, we entered the exercise room.

"Now we'll do Seated Knee-Ups."

"Who's this we?" I teased.

"Don't worry. I get plenty of ab workouts."

"Let's see!" I didn't think he would do it.

Turning his back to the door, Jon lifted his shirt to display smooth skin over a tight, rippled stomach and I understood what a six-pack meant.

"Wow, I want some! Err…one." I said as he dropped his shirt.

"First things first. Now for the Seated Knee-Ups."

I groaned, but it did no good.

"Sit on the edge of this chair, grasp its sides, lean back and extend your legs forward and down. With your feet and knees together, slowly lift your knees to your chest, and then push with the heels to extend them back out. Don't let your feet touch the floor."

That was damn hard! When I finished *my* version of three sets, I rubbed the sweat from my eyes and face.

"Only one more abdominal exercise."

He was merciless.

While I was resting, he brought over a large grey ball about thirty inches in diameter.

"Place the ball at the base of your spine as you lie on it and your feet flat on the floor about shoulder width apart. With your hands behind your head, lift your torso upward using your abdominal muscles. Chin to the ceiling!

"Crunch—crunch—crunch!" He counted the reps.

"I know! No faster than I normally breathe," I interrupted.

"Exhale on the up-crunch. Inhale on the down-crunch. Crunch—crunch—crunch! Keep it up!"

Then at last I was done! He rolled the ball away.

"You've done a great job! Let's finish with stretches. Need some water?"

"Yes…please." My bottle was empty. He grabbed it and left the room, headed to the fountain.

"I'll just have a quick sip of yours…while I'm waiting," I wheezed, and took a long drink. When the water entered my stomach, I relaxed on the cool wooden floor and my consciousness expanded.

Sweeping ripples fan away from my feet. Across the water, island trees fly strings of colorful square flags. I step into a bark boat and row.

Uninterrupted by aquatic spirits wishing to impart knowledge or treasure, the boat lands at a rock-edged path. I step out among the trees and walk to a building whose three floors decrease upward in size like candy boxes stacked one upon another. On the roof, a yellow spire tipped with a white star points skyward.

Decorated beams shade multicolored verandas; cornices project the woodenheads of fantastic animals. I mount the steps, cross the porch, and enter.

Ahead, is a wildcat's painted tear,
and a grey wolf sniffs at my right ear.
Behind, a badger browses my bum,
and a black bear growls in my left eardrum.
Above, a white bird circles in its cruise,
and below, the floor, mole-eaten in small chews.
And as I contemplate these, my friends,
I know my life will never truly end.

I go upstairs. In front of me is an intricate painting. Ten concentric gold rings, each unique, decrease in size inward to encircle a ten-petaled, blue flower. I touch my forehead to the bloom's red center and my mind unfolds.

Then I enter the uppermost floor with its dark blue walls and a ceiling field of yellow stars and lie supine on a maroon rug with interlocking scepters woven of golden thread.

As I stare at the starry ceiling, it dissolves and the heavens open to me. Then a yank from my gut and I let go, join with them, and know the sublime.

Thumping sounds resolved into Jon's footsteps as he returned with my water bottle. The floor under my back was warm.

"What took you so long?" I snarled. I thought he'd been gone forever!

"I stopped to spot Oscar for a set. It took a minute and I apologize. I should have known you'd be thirsty."

What had happened to me? That's twice in two days! I wanted explanations—and soon!

"How about stretching? It would be good for you." He didn't acknowledge my latest lapse. "Since you're on your back, raise your knees to your chest and cross your ankles. Now wrap your arms around your legs below your knees and gently pull downward and stretch your lower back. Then rock your body gently from side to side as if you were a cradle.

"Next lie on your stomach, prone. Place your palms flat on the floor beside your shoulders like you're planning to do a push-up. Gently push your chest and torso up just a little using your arms, keeping your pelvis and legs on the floor. Feel the stretch in your abdominal muscles. Finally, slowly rotate your torso left and right to stretch your muscles."

I was a cobra ready to strike.

"That's it," he said. "We're done."

"But you haven't finished telling me about abs and posture," I said as I returned to prone.

"Haven't you had enough for one day?"

"Not yet, and I'm comfortable here."

"All right," he said as he sat on the floor near me. "Like your mind, the body needs a strong core if it's to accomplish all the tasks you demand. It provides insurance against lower back pain, insures stability when playing sports, and strong abs insure you have power and stamina during sex."

I laughed as he ticked off the insurance dividends I'd receive, and I wondered about the deductibles.

"When a person conditions and adds flexibility to their mid-section, their whole life improves. They develop a positive and refreshing outlook."

Jon continued, "Some believe in the Oriental view that a center of power called the Tan-t'ien is located in your abdomen behind your navel. Through your Tan-t'ien flows your chi, or vital life energy. Strengthening your core enables your life energy to increase and circulate more smoothly throughout your body and mind. That larger energy flow generates well-being, which creates calm and peace of mind. From this comes happiness and satisfaction, and from those come good choices. So, improve your middle to improve your whole. Toning your abs will tone your mind. A strong body core yields a strong mental core.

"And it all begins with good posture. When you stand upright, your ears should be over the center of your shoulders, your shoulders over your hip bones, your hip bones over your knees, and your knees over your ankles. If any are out of alignment, your posture is faulty and problems arise, both physical and mental problems."

"Physical and mental?"

"You're aware of the physical: back, hip, knee, walking and sitting problems. Postural correction can prevent most of these. It's the mental aspect that's more subtle. Your perspective is reflected in your posture and if your posture sags, then so does your outlook. They reinforce each other and when one declines, it pulls the other down with it. A broken person is recognized by his or her broken posture and also by their weak abs. Good posture equals a positive attitude, which is critical for success."

"Do you have any advice on nutrition?" I seemed to be hungry all the time.

"I strive to eat a simple balanced diet consisting of carbohy-drates, protein, and good fat, like nuts, olive and canola oils, and flax seed, for example. I also keep my salt, sugar, and caffeine intake to reasonable levels and try to eat at least 25 grams of fiber every day. In diet, as with the other things in my life, I go with what was written at the doorway of the temple at Delphi in ancient Greece."

"Ancient Greece?" Diet…Greece? Maybe it was a play on words. "What did it say?"

"Well, everyone is familiar with "Know Thyself." But a lesser-known second line read, "Nothing to Excess." These mottos work for everything."

"But it's hard to know how much fat I eat."

"Yes, it can be," Jon said. "But I believe knowing about fat is a key to dietary success. It takes about 3500 calories of energy to burn off one pound of body fat. If you set the exercise bike to a resistance level necessary to burn 350 calories per hour, that's 10 hours of biking per pound. Of course, you use calories doing other things, but you see how much effort it takes just to burn fat.

"And where does this excess body fat come from? Extra calories! I'll give you an example. In some dressings as much as 100 calories per tablespoon come from fat. Let's say you eat one 'extra' tablespoon of dressing per day and don't exercise to burn off these calories. Multiply those 100 by 365 days and you get 36,500 calories which divided by 3500 calories per pound yields over 10 pounds per year. Multiply those 10 pounds by 2, 3, maybe 5 years, and you see how excess body fat is accumulated by eating only 100 extra calories per day."

That was not good news.

"One way I keep an eye on calories is to read the nutrition facts labels found on all food products. If the number I get when I divide the number of fat calories *per serving* by the total number of calories per serving is greater than 20%, then I'm careful about how much of that product I eat. An example would be something that has 200 calories per serving with 80 of the calories coming from fat.

Dividing 80 by 200 you get 0.40, so you see that 40% of the caloric content of this food item is from fat. In my view, true low fat foods have less than 20% of their calories as fat. Now you might think doing these calculations is a lot of work, but which is more work: checking the fat content first, or burning it off your body later?

"And in each exercise session you should burn at least 300 calories, and for a week, 900 to 1200 is best," he concluded.

"I'll remember," I said as I touched Jon's leg.

"And one more thing, Diana," he said. "I also take a daily multivitamin and mineral supplement because much of our food is stripped of its vitamins and minerals by processing. But remember some supplements are toxic at various levels, so if you have questions, ask your doctor before taking anything."

"Thank you," I said. I had a lot to digest and I planned to do cardio before leaving. But as I watched him walk to the trainers' office, I saw a blonde he'd met before was waiting there. They went inside. Together. The door closed and a green wave washed over me.

I went to the locker room to get my bag. But the sad woman I'd seen on my second visit was sitting on the bench. Why, I thought, did these people always sit in front of *my* locker?

"Hello again," she said. "Am I in your way?"

"No. I can get in."

"He finally came home."

"Your husband?"

"Yes."

"That's good."

"Yes, but now he's sitting in the parking lot outside and I don't know what will happen. He thinks I come here to see other men.

True, some of them aren't bad looking, but I only want him. He's just let himself go and I wish we could change things."

"Well, good luck. You know how men are." Or at least I thought I did. I grabbed my bag and headed for the bikes. I looked around for Jon, but he and the blonde woman were still in his office with the door shut.

As I passed the free weights, Oscar was at it and the dumbbells were as big around as my thigh. He finished his set and placed them on the rack. Then he saw me in the mirror and gave a wave. From his gesture I assumed we were pals, but I didn't stop to trade workout tips.

The bike ride was easy and my stomach felt tight. In the last minute, I felt a presence. It was bicycle pants man. Earlier, he'd been wandering the gym and although I wasn't avoiding him, I didn't have anything to say to him either.

"Two Saturdays in a row. That's commitment."

I nodded. A drop of sweat fell from my chin.

"I'm impressed with your determination."

I wanted to blow my nose on his yellow shirt.

"Keep it up and, well…you'll look great."

I didn't think I looked so bad. Go away! I mentally ordered.

But as BPM walked off I couldn't help myself. I just had to watch his butt muscles flex.

Then as I finished my bike journey to nowhere, I saw the sad woman by the front door. I passed by and tried not to notice her.

"Will you walk with me to my car?" she asked as she hurried to keep up with me. "My husband is parked beside it and I want him to see I'm not leaving with a man."

I hesitated, but there was no polite way to avoid it. We women must stick together.

"Fine. Let's go," I said. I stood up straight.

As we approached her car a frothy voice called out, "C'mere." And no, that wasn't French.

Something inside of me solidified. My core was tight and I wasn't going to walk away. As I looked back at the gym, I saw Jon and the tall blonde outside under the awning that proclaimed "Four Palms Fitness Club" in giant red letters. So that's where they are! She looked at him and talked. He looked at me and nodded.

"Hi honey." The sad woman cowered a bit when she said this.

"Get in your car and let's go. I'm tired of you eyeing the guys in there. And from what I see they're weenies." Double-dented crevasses split his eyebrows.

He was, and still could be, a handsome man, but he'd let his life choices get to him. His stomach was distended and probably grooved from the steering wheel. His posture was slumped, his shoulders depressed. And his head stuck out like a rooster ready to peck. He would have been funny, if he hadn't been serious.

I didn't give her time to answer.

"She must love you because I can't see why she works so hard for someone who doesn't appreciate it." I looked into his eyes.

First they filled with shock, and then boiled into anger.

"And who're you? It's none of your damn business. I need her at home with me." He was defiant.

I continued, "Isn't she always there for you? And what do you do for her? What do you do to meet her needs? She has them too."

"I work hard every day," he said, "and I want companionship when I'm home."

"Well, I don't know about that, but she works out here so she can feel good. You could follow her example. Let your anger go. She loves you and wants to stay together more than you do." I didn't know if this last part was true, but said it anyway.

"That's not so." He was defensive.

"It is from what I've seen. Why don't you join her here and grow together? It could be beautiful."

There was a pause—thoughts warred. Finally, he said, "You're right, maybe it could." And I saw the fire go out of his eyes. His face drooped. "She never put it that way."

"Talk about it. Holding onto expectations about what your relationship should be wastes your moments of happiness. And it wastes hers, too. Let go of negativity! Apply loving-kindness! You care for each other. Grow together happily! Don't waste a moment!"

Light entered his eyes. "Let's go home." He looked at his wife.

When I turned to her for the first time in those tension-filled minutes, I saw hope in her face. Maybe it was only surprise.

"Thank you," she said softly and got into her car.

I drove home with the sound of my own voice ringing in my ears, "Let go of negativity! Apply loving-kindness! Don't waste a moment!"

# Chapter Eleven: Illusions and Rivers

*"It was shocking to see I'd worn myself out living up to nothing."*

*Irene* had just removed two purple plastic bags from her locker and opened them.

"What have you got?" I teased as I looked over her shoulder and peeked.

But not to be undone, she showed me. Then let me watch as she methodically tied her red floral halter top, hooked a grass skirt over a red floral swimsuit bottom, and pinned the yellow hibiscuses in her hair.

"Are you going to a party?" I asked with a bit of wonder. What an outfit!

She glanced up briefly as she worked. "Yes, I am. I love to hula and I'm part of a troupe," she said as she painted her mouth, blotted it on a tissue, and then checked her work in the mirror. "We've performed all over the Tampa Bay area. I'm surprised you haven't seen us. It's been about ten years now."

Actually, I thought, maybe I had. Mother, grandmother, and I used to enjoy the hula dancers at a Greek restaurant in Tarpon Springs. Before she died my mother had always wished that she'd learned to hula and my spine chilled to think that maybe Irene had been one of those women she'd admired.

"We've got an early show tonight," Irene continued without noticing, "and then I'll go dancing with my boyfriend. He's a little older and sometimes walks with a cane, but he's not too old to have fun," she turned to me and winked, gal to gal, "all kinds of fun."

"How old were you when you learned to hula?" I asked, remembering my mother.

"Fifty-eight," she answered as she laced her shoes.

"Fifty-eight!" Plus ten, that made Irene at least sixty-eight. I couldn't believe it and from the quick smile on her face, I guessed she knew that.

Still surprised, I asked, "So when did you become a personal trainer?"

"About the same time. I decided I'd learned a lot of good things during my life and I wanted to give some of them back. In here I work with clients the other trainers consider too risky, older people, ones with injuries, and ones recovering from illnesses. I help them to function in their lives and to do the best that they can do." She gathered up her purple bags and closed her locker.

"I'd like to stay and chat some more, young lady, but I've got to hurry," she said as she started toward the door. "It's time to play!" And in a flash of color, she was gone.

"Well, Irene, I think you're the one with the exciting and mysterious life." Then I hurried away too and took my place ready to begin.

"After we finish and if you don't mind, we're meeting a man named Edward," Jon explained on another chest and triceps evening. "My friend Bill wants me to talk with him and although I know we have plans for coffee, Edward doesn't care who hears what he has to say."

"Maybe it's personal." I wanted some alone time with Jon.

"I'd like you there anyway. Edward's in transition. He wants and needs guidance and I think we can help him."

I nodded in agreement.

"So let's get busy. *You* have a lot to do before we go."

I followed his program, sweated, and made any sound that arose. I was less vociferous than men, but no less challenged.

When I finished, I quickly washed my face before dressing, added a liberal dose of deodorant, some reddish-pink lipstick, and a bit of blush. Then I was out the locker room door and as I passed the front desk, Sarah looked up without comment. I hoped she was thinking, "It's the lucky girl!" I *was* lucky. And a little vain too, but so what.

Jon sat in a booth. He'd bought us decaf coffees and a small plate of low-fat, sugar-free cookies. Wistfully, I wished for some wonderfully sweet sugar, preferably from his lips.

There was no sign of our night visitor and my anticipation peaked. Not the stomach-fluttering excitement of a new lover, but I still had an abdominal buzz. It was an evening rendezvous in a darkened coffee house. I put my hands around my cup and looked out from beneath my lowered eyebrows. Maybe the mystery man would impart some serious secrets.

From across the booth Jon watched me with an amused expression. Then I remembered one way to get a man's attention was to tilt your face down and to peer out at him through your eyelashes. This was a come-hither look of submission and willingness. I wasn't too submissive, but I *was* willing.

"How's your coffee? Do you need skim milk or cinnamon?" He'd missed my unintended seductive gaze.

"No, thanks." What I really wanted was whipped cream and chocolate sprinkles. "Our visitor's late," I said.

"He'll be here any minute. I sense his fear and anger."

"How...?"

"Later. Here he comes."

The coffee house door swung open. If done with pleasure, it would have been gusto. But in this situation, tantrum was more appropriate.

A big man with a bullet head covered in short graying hair entered. His darting eyes revealed apprehension at being spotted by a potential enemy. He came and sat next to me.

"The traffic was horrible! A guy cut me off!" he said. Unexpectedly, his voice was mild.

"What's on your mind?" Jon asked.

"Bill suggested I talk to you. He said you might be of assistance to me."

Jon nodded.

"About six months ago when I returned from vacation I discovered my company had had a good-sized layoff. Later they found they'd cut too deep, but to hold down costs, they said we'd have to take on the extra workload. For me this meant sixty-hour weeks with no increase in pay. The company said, "You're lucky you're employed." When I protested, as much for my friends as for myself, I too was axed."

So that was the big mystery, an unemployed man who maybe wanted to be a trainer. But with his confession bravado hissed away and I swore he decreased in size.

"Why don't you tell us the whole story?" Jon sipped his coffee.

"My name is Edward Wooley," he said.

We introduced ourselves and he shook my hand with a quick grasp.

"I remembered you from the party," Edward said to my teacher, "and although we didn't speak, you were the only person there who seemed calm. When I inquired, Bill said you were a gym friend and that you'd helped him."

"You went to a wild bash?" I teased. It seemed unlikely, but possible.

"Not lately. But at one time I used to party with the hardiest," Jon said. "Then I saw I was caught in a cesspool of cravings—both theirs and mine. There was little real fun at some of those gatherings. Add alcohol, and woundology peaked. The conversations, although sometimes subtle, were like badminton played with a rotten avocado. The fruit disintegrated leaving the hard pit and then without warning—whack—you saw stars."

"Couldn't you say anything?"

"Well, people wake up at the rate they wake up. And if someone refuses to let go of their misery, their only relief is to inflict it on others. It's as the old saying goes: misery loves company. So I still party, only a different kind now. My definition of fun has changed and I rejoice in my life."

"I say this as preamble, Edward, because that's what I saw in you. So you can drop pretense tonight because it'll only slow your healing."

Edward continued, "After my layoff I had horrible dreams. Work-mares where no matter how hard I tried, I couldn't complete anything. Once I couldn't find the office, another time I was wandering around naked.

"I saw scenes from my old job—sloppy planning, shock from poor performance, pinning the blame, and punishment for anyone. I saw my former friends laugh whenever they thought of me and I woke up with shouts.

"My days became nightmares as I looked for answers. I went to my old haunts—strip clubs, truck dealers, building supply stores.

But wherever I went, my troubles followed me. I was outside of my old life and I saw myself endlessly searching, never fitting in. I magnified small problems, and I cut people out. It was a paradox, confusion, and unsolvable. I wanted to be accepted, but at every opportunity I shoved it away.

"Finally, I took a temporary job to get back to normal. But not long after I started, I had an accident. I don't know if I was the one that was negligent, but later while lying injured I realized life was very short."

"Yes, indeed," my teacher said.

"Then I recuperated at home. Mornings, I'd hobble around. Afternoons, I'd rest. I was fortunate to have a woman friend who ignored my protests of independence and kept me in groceries. What I did to deserve her, I don't know.

"As I lay in bed, I visualized pictures in the stucco on my bedroom ceiling. I didn't see the things my ex-wife told me about, but I recognized that I was always searching for an answer as to why I'd never felt good about myself.

"And as I watched, the ceiling patterns resolved into an image that slowly faded away. With time, they built a story that started when I was young.

"In the beginning, I believed in myself," Edward continued. "Then as I grew I was taught that no matter what I did, I'd never be good enough. But I could never find out exactly what I was supposed to be as good as. So when I achieved whatever was to make me whole and sane and accepted, the target changed, and no matter how hard I played the game, the end zone eluded me.

"After a lifetime of unsuccessful attempts, mildew coated my personality. Sure, I put on a happy face, but my insides didn't match my outsides and my life was unmanageable. And I found that the mishap at work was only a symptom. My whole frame was bent.

"Some days I'd choke down my lunch and hurry to bed to get a new picture. I was impatient to see how it would all turn out. But I could have seen the results by looking in the mirror. A mirror can only tell what it sees and it doesn't lie. As I looked at myself, it spoke the truth. I'd wasted much of my life and I'd aged myself trying to measure up."

"Did you find out how that happened?" I asked.

Edward looked at me, shaking his head.

"Do you know what a standard is?" Jon asked. "I define a standard as a criterion, something against which something else is benchmarked or compared. Do you understand?"

"Yes," I answered. "For example, for my height a reference says I should weigh a certain amount. But when I find I weigh more, I can choose to feel bad."

"But don't those tables always change?" Edward asked.

"Yes, they do," I said. "They never stay the same and everyone has a different idea about what's correct."

"Right," my teacher said. "It all starts in childhood. Parents and others tell us in various ways that to be acceptable we have to be different from who we really are, and this is not the discipline of teaching skillful choices, but because the ideal is always changing, no matter what we do, we can't ever get it right. The sadness and suffering that results from being unable to resolve this confusion and inner friction builds and continues into adolescence when the need to conform is great and when the major decisions about life's direction are made. Finally, it continues into jobs and careers where being a cog is crucial. We must meet an elusive standard or we're ground down until we do. And so from a young age we can fill with despair. It's true about life being an illusion."

"Is that what you saw, Edward?" I asked.

"Yes, and it's much more graphic when you see it for yourself. It was shocking to see I'd worn myself out living up to nothing."

"So," Edward continued, sadness now in his voice, "I guess I gave myself permission to feel rotten; I gave myself permission to be my own enemy; and I gave myself permission to do whatever it took to relieve the suffering no matter how poor the choice. I didn't look at the consequences. I only wanted relief from the pain. But now I'd like to know, is there a way out? What can I do differently?"

"Yes, there is," Jon said, "and I'll tell you how."

"The solution you seek has three parts. First, you must become aware of the unattainable standard, the unreachable ideal. Ask yourself, 'I'm not good enough as compared to what?' And also ask, 'Is this 'what' anything I should be comparing myself to at all?' You'll usually find it's not and that it's someone else's construct, something they need to feel better about themselves. So get rid of it. You are who you are. It's that simple. Don't waste any more of your life moments chasing something that's running faster than you ever can. And when you slow down and then stop, contentment will fill your life and the despair will be displaced.

"The second part of the solution involves recognizing that being unaware and desperate for relief caused you to make unskillful choices that didn't give you any more than temporary pleasure and may have yielded worse. You've reviewed these over and over in your mind until you think you're doomed to repeat them endlessly. You believe those poor decisions and their sad results are who you truly are.

"This holds no more weight than the empty standard. Look at the choices that have brought you to where you are today. Look, neither judge nor put them into a good or bad context. One teacher said, 'It's all right to look at the past, just don't stare.' You made selections that weren't satisfactory, but now they're past—as gone as your breakfast.

"I tell people to say to themselves, 'That was the best me I knew how to be and now I choose to let it be, because ahead of me I see, a better me for me to be.' So Edward, make your new choices based on loving-kindness and peace, and you won't have to suffer. Your life will spiral out of the darkness of low esteem and into the light.

"A person who's wrapped up in themselves makes a tiny package and so the third part of the solution is to help others. Assist others to improve their lives and bring them tranquility. People balk at this, but it brings the quickest relief.

"When others respond with gratitude its impact changes how you think about yourself. You feel better—literally. Gratitude and appreciation trigger positive changes in brain chemistry. And as you absorb these, your heart, breathing, and brain align and your whole body settles into harmony. So by helping others to achieve happiness, you achieve it for yourself."

When he finished, we sipped our coffees. I had a headache.

"I'll try to work on what you've mentioned," Edward said, "but what can I do right now. Surely you've given advice like this before."

"Yes, I have," Jon said.

"Imagine you're floating in a foggy, swiftly flowing river thronging with people caught in a cold cascade. Around you are many pieces of debris, each prodding with every swirl of the stream. People grasp at this rubble, cling, but the current snatches it away and they cry. Those clutching too tightly or grasping each other go under and disappear. Some are caught in eddies or bashed into boulders; others are swept over falls or snagged by sunken logs. Their moans and screams drown serenity.

"Finally, just before being strangled by your own suffering, you crawl up on the bank gasping like a fish out of water and lying there you flop under the sun and expect to expire. But soon your breath becomes easier and your lungs relax. You're alive! So you stretch, then stand and look around.

"What had been hazy while immersed in the flood is now clear. There are people on the shore, not as many as in the rushing rapids, but they're moving calmly, without panic. They are not hurried and their lives are in order. They proceed with a grace not dependent on who they are or what they have.

"When you look back at the river, the sight is completely different. The agony is unbearable. Humanity is awash with dissatisfactions, engulfed in sorrows, drowning in sufferings. You want to reach in and pull them all out, but the best you can do at first is to be an example, a lighthouse.

"Then as you watch, you see one crawl up onto the bank and lie flopping. Go tell them they're safe, tell them it's unusual to be warm and dry, and tell them many have been through what they're experiencing and all's well. Help them to quiet their breathing so peace can replace their anxiety. Help them to stand so they can take charge of their destiny. Point out paths to follow and allow them to choose what's best suited for them. Act as a gateway to their new life. Then request they do the same for others.

"Edward, you're now on the shore. You're a stranger here, but soon you'll feel more at home. You can jump back in whenever you want, but the longer you're free, the less you'll want to return. Or you'll go only on your own terms.

"The unusual feelings will pass. Exercise. Meditate. Eat healthy food and limit fat, caffeine, sugar, and salt. Get plenty of fresh air and water to purge the toxins. Get into good physical habits because as the body heals so will your mind. The franticness and panicky feelings will dissipate. It also helps to surround yourself with trees and plants. Vegetation is soft and flowing, unlike the hard angularity of human constructions. Being close to natural green rests the mind and returns it to its primordial state. Then it can become aware in its thinking."

"You mentioned meditation," Edward said.

"Yes. Meditation is to the mind as exercise is to the body. It's needed to keep the mind healthy and free from the debris that it accumulates by thinking. But I would recommend the simpler practices to start with until your mind calms and focuses.

"And if you're interested, you could learn several of these at a talk next weekend. Here's my card, call me and I'll give you the details. But it's getting late," Jon said, reaching out his hand. "It was good to see you again and I trust we've helped."

"I've a lot to think about," Edward said, "and I'm getting a headache."

I slid from the booth and also shook hands. Jon gave me a quick hug.

I saw one cookie left on the plate and jammed it into my mouth. Wrong move! I bit down on iron-hard raisins and as I spat out an old filling, I thought I heard it clang when it hit the floor.

"That was fun," I said as liquid pain flowed into my mouth.

"Do you need assistance?" Jon asked.

"No, I don't think so. I'll call my dentist tomorrow and I'm sure she'll see me right away."

We exited and my tooth throbbed with each step so I walked on tiptoes. Cars and trucks were scattered around the parking lot, some with people in them enjoying their coffees. Jon walked me to mine.

"Thanks for a pleasant evening and except for this last part," I said, holding my cheek, "I loved it." And you too, I wanted to add.

"You're welcome. Call me when you get home so I'll know you're safe."

I promised I would, but he still followed me until I got to my complex.

Later, our pillow talk soothed my sore tooth to sleep.

# Chapter Twelve: Dental Drums

*"Extend the quality of equanimity to all. Cool
them with the love from within you."*

$\mathcal{E}$*xpectations* aroused by a dental visit can be colored by fear. My dentist was a tall, tight-faced woman in her mid-forties and although she was expensive, she absorbed new dental information like a sponge and was an expert on all the latest techniques. The filling-fixing business of mine must have seemed routine to her.

Seated on the burgundy leather, chrome-trimmed dental throne I looked out into a thicket of vine-covered pines. To my right, two fancy goldfish bubbled in a framed print hanging above an ornate vase. The chair was illusively comfortable and I might have relaxed if I hadn't thought about the impending procedures. And there was nothing more intimate than having someone in your mouth. The secrets discovered within could reveal your whole life to the intruder and once inside little could be withheld.

Surrounded by mantis-jawed equipment ready to dine on tender tissues, I waited for the doctor to arrive, assess, and execute. Then my traumatized tooth would end its incessant demands.

"How are you today, Ms. Archer?" Dr. Szabo said, extending her hand.

"I'd be fine if I wasn't here," I replied.

The doctor and I played this game every time I came in.

"Let's have a look," she said, ignoring me. The light burst on. A few gentle prods with her pointed metal instruments revealed my dental dramas. The light snapped off and she sighed. In my purse, I imagined my wallet twitched.

"In addition to the old filling on the upper left that fell out, you have a cracked one in the tooth behind it, and a small cavity on your lower right rear molar." She touched my cheeks to indicate where these conditions were hiding their nefarious activities.

"What should we do?" I thought I knew the answer, but asked anyway.

"First, we should fill the small cavity so it doesn't get any larger. Then we'll smooth the hole where you lost the old filling and drill out the cracked filling in the tooth next to it. I'll be able to make both porcelain onlays for those teeth here in the office today. It won't be too bad."

Whether she meant hurt-wise or money-wise wasn't clear. Then she went on to explain how the light pen attached to her computer would image my two teeth and the onsite lab would create onlays to fit the teeth perfectly. A little cement and my tooth troubles would be over.

"Okay, let's do them." Teeth were a pricy pain, but I was attached to mine.

"I'll be giving you shots. Will you want gas also?"

"I'll take it all." Actually I wasn't nervous, but why have any discomfort.

The shots really stung, but after two up and two down, my mouth was comfortably numb. The gas would finish me.

As the dental technician attached the mask and started the flow, she said, "Breath through your nose and go somewhere pleasant." I relaxed, but squinted my eyes for a moment when the dentist snapped on the light.

A yellow melon floated over a mountain meadow of waist-high grass and dark green brush: the sun glowed in a cloudless cerulean sky.

Somewhere in my mind sat a woman in taupe business clothes, a mantis-drill whining in her mouth. Wherever she was, it was real to her. Just as sunbasking here was real to me.

The meadow was partially ringed by a ragged dentition of peaks. A slab of rust-colored rock blocked the open end. Aprons knit from stone shards spread wide at the feet of the mountains and grayish-white boulders, some larger than houses, were scattered about. Where these behemoths chatted communally, dense islands formed in the midst of the meadow.

From one such island emerged a woman. Skin-tight clothes blended her into the weeds and I knew wherever she went, she'd blend in there too. I didn't try to hide and she came straight to me. The thick grass swished against her legs.

"Rain is coming," she said and took my hand. Her skin was soft and warm; her eyes were clear and bright.

As we walked together, storm clouds hurried from behind the peaks and a pewter ceiling lowered on the meadow basin. I saw before me a small lake, its surface dancing with the wind. By the shore, reeds whistled in the shower.

Then we angled away from the lake and ascended a debris-strewn slope. Far above the water the ground flattened and the track stopped at the face of a steep cliff. Hand and foot-holds cut into its vertical surface allowed me to follow her as we climbed up to a small room. It was not a cave, but more like a curved surface. Above, a rock beak kept the alcove dry, and its jutting sides deflected the bite of the wind.

Wrapped in blankets, we reclined on the smooth limestone and I saw lake, meadow, the stony apron, and above them, the far rampart. Ghosts of mist wavered in my view and I dozed. There was a whine.

It seemed only a few minutes had passed when I awoke alone. The wisps had run away and the sun illuminated a large figure watching me from the distant rock wall.

The light hurried with the turning Earth and I saw either a man or a woman. The figure's clothing was rusty red trimmed with bands of green and yellow, and the hair was a shiny dark river that spilled down over its right shoulder. There was a headdress of tan, gray, and white feathers with a multicolored beaded band tying it around the head. The left hand gripped a carved brown staff and a deep golden bowl filled the other upturned palm. A serene smile creased its face and its eyes were jet jewels set into the folds.

Then as the sunlight shifted, the figure stepped from the rock wall, strode down the inclined talus apron, and out across the valley. It sat on one of the rock islands that now looked like scattered stools.

A low hum, then a rhythmic voice spoke to my heart.

"You are re-aiming your intentions. You are re-energizing your mind. You are rebuilding your body. You are relinquishing your unskillful choices. You are recognizing and redefining your happiness." Slow drumming. "Now, ReBecome.

"Filled with loving-kindness, joy, compassion, and serenity, you nurture. From this wholeness of strength and gentleness, seen as a blue-white sun, you move." The drum tempo increased.

"Take this sun, enfold someone close and give them a share, energize their inner beauty. See them with happiness.

"Expand your sun to include your dislikes, those who have put their sufferings into your life. See them with bliss." Stronger drumming.

"Enlarge your blue-white blaze to envelop all beings—people, animals, and plants—in your city and in your country. Feed them with joy.

"Then enclose our planet. Put the world within your halo. Extend the quality of equanimity and the relief from agony to all. See areas of anger as inflamed boils. Cover them with your hand and cool them with the love from within you. See them healed." The drums reached a crescendo.

"Teach others to awaken. Teach them to ReBecome. And teach them to teach others."

The figure moved the staff from side to side and offered me the golden bowl that geysered plumes of brilliant blue-white light. I reached out with both hands and as it touched my fingers, the drums ceased.

I opened my eyes and saw vine-coated pines.

"Is everything all right?" The dental technician was fanning my face with a manila folder. "You were moving your arms and breathing hard. I didn't want you to hurt yourself."

"I'm fine." The vision faded like the after images from a strobe. I felt the bowl in my lap.

"You can leave whenever you're ready."

"Are my teeth fixed?" I'd remembered why I was there. Dr. Szabo was nowhere in sight.

"Everything went smoothly. You were asleep."

"Hardly."

"What?" She looked confused.

"Nothing. Give me a couple of minutes and I'll go."

"Take your time. 'Bye."

I reclined my head and tried to reconstruct what I'd experienced.

"What's going on with me?" my mouth mumbled as I drove back to the office. I was afraid to close my eyes. These sudden daytime adventures were unsettling. At night you expected vivid dreams, but not during the day.

"What's their purpose? Are they helping or hurting?" I slurred to myself. But while waiting at a red light, I saw that after each episode I'd expanded, become more aware.

Then as a sharp horn honk cut into my thoughts, I bit the inside of my numb cheek and tasted warm blood.

"Jon better have answers. Now!"

# Chapter Thirteen:
## Compassion on the Sand

*"We soon find that many of our problems we have caused for ourselves."*

"*Eeeuu!* Picnics are bor-ring!" I once heard a childhood friend say to his parents. This was different from the math in my home where fresh air plus being together equaled happy.

When I was young and my family was all together, we went on picnics while our neighbors all hurried in separate directions. I'd always wondered what that rush to nowhere got them. If happy memories made with each other weren't the most important things in life, then what was?

On that Sunday, Jon and I had made plans to go the beach. Finally. And as I sat on my apartment steps in the sun and listened to the cabbage palms rustling in the humid mid-day breeze, I awaited his arrival with giddy anticipation. Sitting there was a compromise between not wanting to appear too excited by waiting by my car versus not wanting to appear disinterested by waiting inside the apartment, or by not being ready. And getting dressed that morning had been a battle.

I'd searched and searched for my sexy beach shorts and finally determined that they had to be in a box on the top shelf of my very cramped closet. Then I'd cautiously removed box after box until one of them broke apart as I held it overhead and showered me with pieces of photo albums, old love letters, and recipes torn from thirty-year-old magazines. All had been roach chewed leaving dark brown stains, and the roach droppings and musty smell made me sneeze. But in the very next box I found what I wanted. Relieved, I kicked the whole mess into the closet and shoved the door shut.

Then I tried to pull the beach shorts on, slowly. "So far so good," I said as they slid up my legs. But when I tried to ease them over my bottom I heard a sound worse than, "Hey, baby!" With a diet-prompting rip, the rear seam split. I sat on the side of the bed, looked at the tear, and even stuck my fingers through it and wiggled them in my face. Discouraged, I thought about calling Jon and canceling, but I really wanted to make a special memory with him.

Then I looked in the mirror on the back of my bathroom door. My stomach was smaller, but my bottom seemed bigger. I breathed slowly and I thought, what would cause this? I wasn't cooking high-calorie meals as much and I was definitely eating a lot more fruits and vegetables. I drank strange tasting fiber shakes and had practically worn out my calculator doing fat content calculations. Then I remembered he'd told me my program wouldn't make me super muscular, but he'd also said it'd take a while to get rid of the excess fat on my body. I'd increased the size of my butt muscles, but hadn't decreased the amount of fat over them. I was even bigger than before! All my exercise, all my improved eating habits, and all my hard gym work wasn't enough. I could just give up on ever being seductive. I fought back tears because I didn't want red eyes when he arrived.

Then the answer and relief came to me. I thought about how Jon had said if I stuck to my program, the fat would soon have nowhere to hide and then it'd be gone for good. I'd just have to be patient and not quit. In the past, hurry-up changes had never lasted. But being patient was not easy. My grandmother had said, "You either learn patience, or become one." Frustrated, I dug around in my dresser for a pair of stretchy shorts and then belted them tightly to accentuate my somewhat narrower waist.

At last I saw him! He was wearing dark trunks and a sky blue tee shirt with a picture of a big green turtle. Since my dental experience, my senses were sharper, more in focus, and I saw his body heat parting the air as he approached. Whorls spun behind him.

"Good afternoon, Diana!" Jon bounded up the stairs to where I sat.

"And what's this?" he said, looking at the basket on the step next to me. "It's beautiful!"

"It's a picnic basket from my childhood and it has lots of special memories inside."

"We'll make new ones today," he said. It was hard to see his eyes through his sunglasses, but I knew they were lit. Jon was not someone who smiled with his mouth while his eyes remained cold or unfocused. I put on my sunglasses too.

We drove mostly in silence. Not a strained "what's wrong" silence, but a quiet that was comfortable for both of us. It could have been broken any time without fear of reprimand. Later, the Celtic music Jon played made me think of stately trees and wild things, and of warm sunlight and flowing water. We were going to a happy destination on the gulf beaches. But as in life, he reminded me, the journey itself was also happiness and people forget that.

Later at the shore, we carried the basket between us as we walked across the white sand and had we been more than friends, it would have been romantic. I wanted to be more, but Jon was different from other men I'd known and I was glad. Most were in a hurry and I knew they needed that sometimes, and it was all right. But a balance with my needs would have made a truer partnership. Jon wanted what was best for me and understood me in ways I couldn't yet comprehend, but he didn't exploit that and I felt secure.

We found a spot close to the surf between two dunes crowned with waving sea oats and yellow morning glories and laid out the blanket. Then we feasted on an almond-crusted cheese ball with black pepper crackers, crab salad sandwiches made with pecans and dried cherries, and for dessert we, rather I, had strawberries dipped in real milk chocolate. When we'd finished eating, we gazed out to sea, ginger beers in hand.

"Thank you for bringing me here." I prodded his foot with mine.

"You're welcome. It's nice to see the horizon. It gives you perspective." He fell silent.

But I wanted to talk.

"When we were having dinner," I said, "you mentioned that two things are important to you in relationships. I've thought about loving-kindness and how to generate more of it in my life. But now I'd like you to tell me about the other one."

"Maybe you'd like a rest today."

"Well, it's either tell me, or you have to give me more, and I mean specific, details about what I saw in the dental dream." I wanted to sound menacing, but it didn't work. I'd tried to talk about my episode during a workout, but he'd wanted to wait, and for me, waiting was suffering.

"We'll talk about compassion," he said.

We folded our towels to make pillows and stretched out on the blanket. We could see where the sky and water kissed. I hoped we would too. I moved closer.

"Many believe compassion is pity or sympathy," Jon began, "and while it can include these, what it actually means is that you understand that others suffer as you do. Everyone, no matter who, suffers equally from the same things: we want everything to live up to our expectations; we want to get whatever we want and we want to get it quickly; we don't want to lose something we like; and we don't want to get anything we don't like. It sounds simple, but it's profound. Every action we take is an attempt to satisfy those things. Every thought, every action.

"This is important because the miserable feelings we each have are identical. The suffering is the same inside each of us. For example: Do you enjoy being dissatisfied and disappointed? Do you enjoy distress? Do you want to suffer? Your answers will all be 'No!' and so will everyone else's. No one wants these things; no one wants to endure them. Yet understanding that we all desire the same things and that we all suffer in the same ways when we don't get them, creates a universal bond between us. This is the only true equality.

"So, compassion begins with this knowledge and its application is simple. Because we understand what it's like to be unhappy and because we know others are also, a primary practice is to *avoid doing anything that causes or adds to the unhappiness of another.* We must think before we act or speak: Will this decrease their happiness? If the answer is yes, the action or speech should be avoided. But if the actions or words increase your peace and also your friend's, then it is a compassionate act.

"So how do you nurture compassion? Start by being compassionate to yourself—first. Look at your life, don't judge, only look. How much dissatisfaction do you experience? How much mental pain? Recognize these things occur, but also recognize a lot of this anguish comes from our own personal choices about how to live each day. We have a strong tendency to blame others, but we soon find that many of our problems we have caused for ourselves. So be forgiving to yourself and don't waste life's moments. Because you originate many of your own troubles, you can stop them.

"Now I'll tie it all together. To be truly satisfying, a relationship must contain loving-kindness to allow the development of genuine friendliness and gentleness. And it must contain compassion so each understands the experience of suffering is common to both and that nothing must be done to cause or increase the distress of the other. Or as one of my teachers said, 'Another interpretation of the Golden Rule could be: Do unto others as *they* would have you do unto them.'

"With these qualities you'll have a prosperous relationship," Jon concluded, "and remember these also apply every time two or more persons come together and they include your relationship with yourself."

"In the past it's been hard to have a good relationship with myself," I said, "but now when I feel a twinge inside, I check to see if I've been too critical. If I have, I apply loving-kindness and then switch my thoughts to something else."

"That's excellent," Jon said. "And also be aware that when we scrape really hard on ourselves and do it for a long period of time, it forms a callus which can cause us to miss out on the pleasures of life. And once formed, these habits are difficult to break unless we see there's more to living than self-chastisement."

"I'm so glad I met you," I said with feeling. "I'd almost given up, but now I'm hopeful."

"I'm pleased too. But realize that hope is crystallized fear so don't only hope, take action so whatever you're hoping for comes to pass. Without action to back it, hope is useless."

"I'll remember." Then, smiling, "I *hope* you're happy being with me, and if necessary I'll take *action* to make it so." I poked his arm.

"No action is necessary, Sweetheart. After all, happiness is generated from within and no matter what others do, no one can take it away. They can add to it, but they can't take it away."

"Is that really true?" I'd wanted a sweet nothing in response. Sweetheart, again?

"Yes, it is. Once you put your life on an even keel, like that sailboat out there, you build up a reservoir of peace that carries you through the roughest storms. And once it's in place, like ballast, no one can blow your life off any course you set for it. They can help you get to your destination, they may even join you on board, but they'll have only as much effect on your passage as you allow them.

"People talk about internal strength and fortitude, guts, but all that means is that you're secure within yourself and have sufficient contentment to fearlessly face life. And if you're not afraid, no one can persuade you to do unskillful things. So each morning say to yourself: 'Just for today, I am unafraid!' Do this one day at a time and it'll soon become part of you."

"But how do you develop an unshakable reservoir?" I asked.

"Be compassionate to yourself and it will build. Do you remember the talk I mentioned to Edward? It's next Saturday and if you'll join me you'll gain additional knowledge. The topic is the nature of the mind and how, when you understand it, you can make skillful choices."

"I'd love to go. But tell me, how do you make skillful choices in your life? Is there a secret?"

"No. There's no secret. The truth is not to identify with your mind. I won't go into detail now because you'll get plenty of explanation. But I will say that when you have a clear understanding of your mind and how it functions it becomes easier to make the right choices—the most valuable trait of life and the single most important skill a parent can teach a child. *Everything* in their life depends on it.

"I'll pick you up at 6:30," Jon concluded.

"I'll be ready, unless I have to work. I'll let you know."

"You wouldn't work on Saturday night?"

"I can't be certain. Sometimes Mr. Dawl doesn't want to stay home with his family so he invents excuses to be at the office. Everyone has to be there so he can act important and we all have to participate to keep our jobs. Plus business is down right now and so we don't quite know what to expect. There's a lot of tension and all the managers do is create more fear."

"But why that particular job?"

"Well, I've been there a long time, my friends are great, and it used to be a good place to work. But now management doesn't have a lot of compassion and I don't know why because it doesn't make their jobs any easier and it certainly doesn't help the company."

"I can tell you why. It's because causing fear in another gives those supervisors a momentary pleasure," he said, "but since this fades rapidly, the action has to be repeated—often. In contrast, the benefits that come from helping others can last a lifetime and beyond. It seems a simple choice, but hardly anyone makes it.

"I'm still wondering. Why don't you leave?" Jon asked.

"Sometimes I think I should, but then I tell myself, 'If I could just get my promotion, everything would be better.' Besides, leaving would require a lot of effort and an inner voice says, 'Quitters never win.' Or it says, 'I'm not good enough to find something else.' But since I've met you I've started to realize how this job has crushed my creativity and how it's addicted me into believing what goes on there is normal and healthy.

"But I've made my decision about Saturday. I'm going with you. I'm not working late. Mr. Dawl can just go to a nudie bar." But a thought arose.

"In fact," I said. "I'm honored to go with you. I'll wear my new black satin mini, a white lace bustier under a sheer blouse, and C-L-M-P's."

"What? Ah...no. But something casual would be appropriate," Jon said.

"I'm kidding. I'll dress for the occasion."

He looked perplexed.

"What's wrong? I was joking."

"C-L-M-P's?"

I laughed. He didn't get it.

"They're shoes. Come Love Me Pumps. I'm sure you've seen them."

"I...well. Yes, I guess I have. I hadn't heard them called that. What size do you wear?"

"I wear an eight."

"An eight! If they have eight-inch heels, how do you walk, or love?"

We laughed.

"Casual clothes will be fine," Jon repeated.

For a moment he'd thought I was serious. But I had no CLMP's, or sheer blouse and bustier, or even a satin miniskirt, but from the expressions on his face he must have been imagining how I'd look wearing them. I'd search my trash. I was sure I'd gotten a lingerie catalog recently.

The day ended as the Milky Way appeared in the deep blue sky.

In bed that night I dreamed I was weaving a starry basket of loving-kindness and compassion to hold my love.

# Chapter Fourteen:
## Flowers in the Open Sky

*"When we have our thoughts, our lives can be smooth and peaceful, but when our thoughts have us, our lives are full of anger, negativity, and greed."*

*For* an entire week, I had endured Mr. Dawl's slobbery commentary about my new auburn hair color and smaller-sized clothes. And then he made us work on the weekend again. On Saturday morning he was civil, but at lunch he'd gotten tight and when I told him I had to leave at five, he turned unpleasant.

"You're seeing that trainer boy again tonight, aren't you Ms Archer?" Mr. Dawl gushed, almost snorting.

"We're going to a party," I said. It was a discussion, but party sounded more exciting to me.

"Well, what kind of soiree is it?" He strutted back and forth. "Will the women dance or strip? Or do you sprawl around nude watching porno movies and groping?" Lust brimmed in his eyes.

While Mr. Dawl spoke, my mind marveled at how you could get used to disgusting behavior when you were around it all the time.

"No," I said firmly and embarrassed. "We're going to study some material." What precisely, I didn't know, but I'd make up something if necessary.

"Erotic pictures perhaps?"

"Just writing."

"Well, that's a bummer and a damn bore!"

His mind was grinding full tilt.

"Maybe it's BYOB," he said with a low snicker, squinting as he swayed.

"I don't think there'll be alcohol. We're not taking any."

"What? I don't mean booze!" he exclaimed, feigning shock. "Where do you live, Diana? In a hole? Just so you know, BYOB means Bring Your Own Body. You bring your body to the party to share with everyone," he reveled. His chins waved back and forth. Then, "Maybe I should go along and share too." He gawked at me, wishes conveyed by lewdness.

I wanted to throw up, but managed to say nothing.

"Well, haaavvveee fun," he said. His laugh diminished to sarcasm. "I hope your trainer boy has what it takes to satisfy you."

He did, but my face was flat.

When he saw that he couldn't make me angry, he slouched away. His parting comment, "Don't wear yourself out. We may have to work tomorrow."

Sunday, my phone was off.

I'd asked Jon to drive that Saturday night because I wanted to be seen as his date. I knew this wasn't exactly the case, but I couldn't help myself.

As we rode over the causeway bridge, we left the traffic of Tampa behind. I studied Jon's face as we drove and thought his mom must have been terrific to have raised such a wonderful son. I'd felt sad for him when he'd told me during a workout that both his parents had passed away leaving him with only his sister and a couple of distant cousins.

After the long causeway, we drove through a semi-wooded area of large homes. We were near Safety Harbor and not too far from where the old Kapok Tree restaurant stood.

As we passed through the new neighborhood of giant houses, Jon said he imagined debt-grimaced faces watching us from behind the closely mowed lawns. I'd envisioned spa tubs and large, gourmet, eat-in kitchens with fireplaces. The model looked open, but he didn't want to stop.

When we arrived at our destination, a smaller one-story house, we walked up the slate path, through the wrought iron gates, and into a patio with large sago palms and pots of sansevieria, whose yellow-edged leaves resembled green flames. We stood in front of the ornate, red front door next to a copper-tarnished-to-turquoise water feature and Jon rang the bell as he pointed to four large brass cranes among the greenery. "They bring good fortune," he said.

When the red door with its polished brass handle opened, our hosts, who were a pleasant middle-aged couple, welcomed us inside to join a dozen or so other people that had already arrived. They were a diverse group in all ways and relaxed on deep lavender and white sofas and on multi-colored pillows on the floor. It was a huge living room with two walls made entirely of glass and the third one with a large, white brick fireplace with a long raised hearth. No one was sprawled—or naked.

Edward came over and greeted us and then returned to talk with an attractive, dark-tanned woman.

Candles scented the air and through the two glass walls I saw a caramel-colored cocker spaniel panting and running through the heat in the broad, fenced backyard. Palms were grouped in clumps along the edge and in islands with citrus trees, the specific types of which I was uncertain. Andrea, however, would have been able to tell them apart easily. She was a Florida native and took great pleasure in pointing out the different plants. One of her past boyfriends had been a kind of horticulturist and she was proud of her palm smarts, as she called them.

As we walked farther into the room, I saw fruit and cheese trays scattered on tables. Juice, iced herbal teas, and coffee were on the large island counter between the kitchen and dining area. Everything was low-key and pleasant, and I felt comfortable.

My first surprise of the evening arrived in the kitchen as I poured some orange juice. Jim walked in! He'd cleaned up really well—nice slacks, dark shoes, and a blue shirt to go with his eyes—and his new contact lenses. But this was immediately followed by another shock—bicycle pants man! My cup overflowed.

BPM spoke first, but neither he nor Jim seemed amazed to see me. It must be a guy thing. If you're surprised, you lose points.

"Well, look who's here!" BPM said. "It's Diana, and she looks hot! Jim, turn down the air conditioning!"

I'd dressed for my teacher, but I liked that BPM had noticed. He'd cleaned up nicely too.

"That juice for me?" BPM asked with a grin best described as ingratiating.

"Get your own. This one's for Jim." I handed it to him. At last, a surprised man.

"Thanks," Jim said. "Jon told us about you, but he must not have mentioned us." His grin matched BPM's.

"He didn't, and I wonder what else he hasn't mentioned."

"I'm sure there's something," Jim said, jokingly looking around from floor to ceiling and ceiling to floor.

And I knew there might be, but I wasn't asking. I'd lost enough points.

"Let's go check out the hot tub," BPM said.

We followed him out the sliding glass door and into the backyard where the dog jumped and drooled.

It was a big tub made from real redwood or cedar under a white gazebo. A trellis of bright pink bougainvillea on one side secluded it from the house.

"How romantic," BPM said and then added in a stage whisper to me, "Let's ditch Jim, strip, and splash."

Another time his remark might have been a little flattering, but after the sour conversation with my boss, I really wasn't amused. Then in silence I realized Mr. Dawl's intention had been to create dissatisfaction in me so I'd wish I'd spent the evening with him. And as I thought about that, I decided I needed to find the bathroom so I could be alone for a few minutes and try to generate some loving-kindness.

I walked back inside, down a long dim hall, and as I reached the corner I ran—bump—into a man. Under the light of a wall sconce, I looked up into familiar grey-green eyes, ones with quiet and depth. It was the man from the restaurant bar! The one I'd run out on months ago! I was amazed and felt saliva on my lips. He looked me up and down, took me by the shoulders, and then gave me a hug. His beard tickled my cheek and he was wearing wonderful cologne. It must be a male version of the Persuader, my dazed mind said.

"At last we meet again, my friend Diana. And I am so happy to see you. Allow me to reintroduce myself. I'm Stefan Sansome." He shook my limp hand.

"I can *not* believe this coincidence," I said, and almost gestured. "What are the chances of running into you again?"

"Indeed," he said with a twinkle in his eye. "We'll have to see."

"But what are you doing here?" I asked. "Are you here to listen to Jon?"

"Yes. And I'm looking forward to it. He's a good teacher and getting better."

"Yes, he is," I said. Then, "Do you know anyone else here tonight?" People had started to settle in the living room.

"I've met some, but not everyone. I know your teacher though."

"Well…has he told you anything about me?" Eagerness—clothed.

"He's told me you ask lots of questions and that you're the brightest and most beautiful person he's ever met."

"He did?" I exclaimed-whispered. "Jon said that?" Eagerness—naked.

"Yes. But we'll visit later. It's time for the lecture to begin."

Stefan offered me his arm and as we entered the living room there was applause. I saw BPM gaping. "So there!" I thought.

My teacher sat on a deep plum pillow and beside him was an empty gold cushion. Stefan escorted me to the cushion and then sat on the raised hearth. Jon placed his hand on mine.

With an "aum" Stefan cleared his throat. "Welcome, friends!" Stefan was the speaker!

"I want each of you to be happy," Stefan began. "I am. And I'll share my knowledge so you can be too. Tonight we will look at the difficulties caused by the mind, the remedies, and conclude with three easy to learn healings.

"From personal experience and wide-ranging study I've learned that a person's mind is composed of two parts. There is the 'Mundane Mind' with its ceaseless wants, aversions, and concepts. And there is the 'Open Sky Mind,' like the sky above: vast, without beginning or end, a peaceful, joyous spaciousness.

"Using this analogy we see that all the thoughts, needs, animosities, and dissatisfactions of the Mundane Mind are but ephemeral clouds floating within the Open Sky Mind, in the same way clouds float through the open sky above our heads, and we see that the happiness we experience on Earth is determined by whether we live within our cramped Mundane Mind or fly free in our Open Sky Mind.

"As we grow, we develop both types of minds. But through cultural conditioning the desires of the Mundane Mind receive maximum attention. The results of this one-sided focus are obvious. How many of us are happy long-term? Few. Most are ceaselessly searching, getting, attaching, and rejecting. And why do we all engage in these activities with such single-minded determination? To relieve the anguish we have on a deep level from not knowing our true selves, from not comprehending our consciousness. This anxiety manifests as uneasy feelings that things are not quite right, that things are not quite complete, and that no matter how hard we work, how much we spend, how fast we hurry, or who we are with, they never will be. But by understanding our all-knowing Open Sky Mind, relief can be attained, along with answers to the questions: 'Who am I? Why am I here? How can I be content? Where do I go in the end?' And long ago, although I didn't always realize it on a conscious level, it was the frantic search for relief from those questions that was the driving force in my life."

"Does everyone have these concerns?" asked a woman on the sofa.

"Yes, they do. Most of the time throughout history, however, the focus has been on surviving and staying alive each endless day. But when basic needs are satisfied those questions always arise. And if we apply with diligence the universal principles we will discuss tonight, the lives of all would be elevated to the level at which we could unravel their answers—together.

"Now let's look at the Mundane Mind.

"The Mundane Mind thinks, conceives, and plots. It thirsts to acquire and it hastens to dispose. It's angry when it doesn't get its wants, it points in blame, it whines and cries, and it indulges in self-pity and hopelessness. The Mundane Mind creates such disruptive thoughts that our mental structure explodes like a shack of twigs and matches. This cranial eruption expels mind debris: anger, fear, and greed, outward at the speed of thought. And those closest to us, persons, animals, and nature, take the impact. Unending streams of ramblings radiate from the Mundane Mind. And it's said the Mundane Mind is as disruptive as a drunken monkey infested with lice.

"But the Mundane Mind can also contain thoughts of happiness, thoughts that bring us some relief from the grasping and angry negativities that are so often life's focus. And a few of these pleasant thoughts may last awhile, but most do not. They persist only as long as our focus, a person or thing, is fresh. When the newness changes with time the Mundane Minds looks for flaws. And that justifies our search for the next new person or object on which to base our happiness. These quests take many forms, and can last a lifetime.

"Now, while these facts are disheartening, there is relief from the tyranny of the Mundane Mind and there is a saying: the mind makes a wonderful servant, but a terrible master. So when you see that the ceaseless demands of the Mundane Mind bring you little lasting satisfaction, you make choices to loosen its grip. And having your mind as your helper instead of your jailor brings you peace."

He took a breath and said we'd break for ten minutes.

At first no one moved, then a woman went into the kitchen, and we were released from the spell. There was a collective sigh and everyone whispered. I reclined and stared at the ceiling before closing my eyes.

Then my lips felt a warm, thick pressure. Something round and sticky wanted inside. They opened and I tasted fire. Jon had fed me a cherry tomato dipped in pepper cheese sauce. I wanted to ask about Stefan, but before I could, everyone re-gathered and he began again.

✳

"My friends, when we view our lives from the larger perspective of the Open Sky Mind we find clinging to any passing thought leads to unhappiness. Let's see why that is true.

"To comprehend the Open Sky Mind we must understand that our core being, sometimes called the Self, is not our thoughts. We have thoughts and the results of these thoughts can lead to action. However, *we are not our thoughts*. This will be disturbing to some, who may ask, 'If I'm not my thoughts, then who am I?'

"I will clarify this with an analogy. We are no more our thoughts than we are our breath. Our breath passes in and out of us and we must have our breath to live. Our thoughts pass in and out of our minds and we will have thoughts for as long as we live. However, we are neither our thoughts nor our breath, nor anything else that passes through our minds or bodies.

"Continuing, we find our mind looks in two directions, outward and inward. Culturally we are taught to look outward. Reversing this process and looking inward we ask ourselves, 'Who is having this thought?' By doing that simple process we see someone separate from the thought is having the thought and we see the thought is not the person having it. If we truly were our thoughts we would not be able to make that distinction. There would be no difference between the thinker and the thought. The person doing the thinking would not be able to say, 'I am having a thought.' And while this is an obvious fact, few discern it, and fewer still gain the perspective to use this knowledge to improve their lives.

"To use a different analogy, our thoughts are like objects you pick up. You examine the object as it rests in your hand, then you put it down to pick up the next one. You do not identify with the object. You know it is not you. The same process applies to our thoughts. A thought arises, abides for a time, and then ceases as another arising thought replaces it. This is the process of thinking and no matter how fast the sequence, all thoughts go through the same progression: arising, abiding, ceasing.

"When I apply these analogies, I see the Mundane Mind is the thoughts I have. And the Open Sky Mind is the thinker of these thoughts. The Mundane Mind is like the objects we hold in our hand and the Open Sky Mind is the owner of our hand. The Open Sky Mind perceives the thought process and knows it is not the thoughts. It knows thoughts are but a small part of its vastness.

"So do not hold onto thoughts. The key to freedom is to shift your awareness away from the Mundane Mind and into the Open Sky Mind and to see your thoughts only as clouds passing through it. When I apply this insight to my life the relief is phenomenal. A quick example is all the: you should—be perfect—hurry up—please me—try harder—yes but—I was just—I was only, squalls blow away.

"Once you see your thought for what it is, a simple mental motion within a much larger framework, you do not have to identify with the thought, react to it, or cling to it. You notice its arising, abiding, and ceasing. Then you simply let it go. In a similar manner both placid and stormy clouds pass through the sky overhead, yet the sky remains unattached and unaffected. You can hold on to a thought no more than you can hold on to your breath, no more than the blue sky above can hold on to a cloud.

"Some other examples will demonstrate the benefits you'll gain from being unattached to your thoughts.

"If an angry thought arises in your Mundane Mind you can say, 'That is an angry thought. It is not me and I can let it go without reacting.' Think how much suffering that will stop within you and for others.

"If a wanting thought appears you can say, 'That is a wanting thought. It is not me and I can let it go without acquiring.' Think how much of the agony of debt, for example, can be avoided by letting go of wanting thoughts.

"If a thought appears like 'I'm not good enough, thin enough, smart enough, or whatever enough,' you can say, 'That is only a thought.' It is not me and I can let it go.' This will relieve many of the problems associated with feeling bad about yourself and all the issues that go with them.

"If judging, comparing, or needing to know why, thoughts arise you can let them go because they are not you. Many interpersonal issues would be resolved by not being attached to those divisive thoughts.

"To summarize, when this process is understood, most thoughts, and especially the disturbing ones, take on much diminished roles in your life.

"Over time, by knowing your thoughts are not truly you and that you don't have to react to any unless you choose, you develop deep serenity and peace of mind. Within this peaceful space, free from the frantic demands for attention your Mundane Mind makes, you perceive and come to know who you are and your life's purpose becomes clear. You develop into a person whose thoughts, speech, and actions are all in alignment. You see the big picture and this prevents problems and mistakes. For example, you stop thinking one thing, saying a second, and doing a third. This is one solution to the unmanageability problems discussed in many helping programs.

"You also find you naturally choose the paths of kindness and compassion instead of other paths that are more hurtful. And from this choice, genuine happiness results and because it is not based on attachment to things derived from fleeting thoughts, it is long lasting.

"My friends, I understand this information is easy to convey, but it will take practice to put it into effect. There are, however, three simple and fun methods by which you can attain these goals. My friend Jon will explain them after another break."

There was a round of applause followed by questions.

"This is what I needed." Edward said, moving to sit next to me. "After coffee the other evening, I decided to take a vacation. I called the woman who'd been helping and asked her to go with me. We're going to have a wonderful time and eat every meal out."

"That's terrific. Maybe someday I'll have the time and money and someone to go somewhere," I said, mostly to myself.

Jim came over and knelt on one knee. "Having fun?" His eyes were happy.

"It's a lot of information, but I'm enjoying myself."

"I see you still have Jon's pen."

"I use it for my notes."

Our host rang a chime and everyone returned to their places. Then to my surprise, Stefan sat next to me. Jim gave me a thumbs-up.

Then it was my teacher's turn to talk. I'd never shared Jon with so many people and I was proud of him.

"You've heard that when we have our thoughts, our lives can be smooth and peaceful," Jon began, "but when our thoughts have us, our lives are full of anger, negativity, and greed.

"Now you will learn three easy techniques for focusing on the Open Sky Mind so when thoughts arise, you will recognize them as thoughts and not become attached. This allows you to make loving and compassionate choices.

"I'll use simple, yet profound, meditations, and once you've achieved success in slowing down your rabid stream of thoughts, you can go on to more involved visualization practices if you so desire. I urge you, however, not to be put off by the lack of complexity of the following three. I've found simpler and easier exercises done regularly are highly effective because they give the Mundane Mind little with which to produce thoughts. And the fewer thoughts created, the sooner the mind calms.

"Our first technique will clear your mind. Sit or lie in a quiet place, get comfortable, and close your eyes. Try not to have any sensory distractions. Your thoughts will be running like a herd of wild horses. Do not be concerned or judgmental toward yourself. You cannot tame this heated stampede instantly. Just sit quietly without moving and let your thinking go racing on. But while you do this, visualize cool water bathing your brain and flowing over your unbridled thoughts as they arise, abide, and cease. Allow this calming flow of water to wash over each thought until they become like bubbles in the pool of liquid now surrounding your mind. Soon your mind will slow and you'll be able to see you are not your thoughts and that they have a distinct beginning and end. They bubble to the surface, pop, and then go without a trace. From this cool mind you say to yourself, 'here comes a thought and there goes a thought.' You have no attachment or emotional involvement. You don't have to do anything but watch. With continued practice, this swiftly releases attachment to thoughts.

"My second method involves using your breath and voice. Sit or lie down and relax. Your eyes can be open or closed and there should be a gentle smile on your face. Inhale through your nose and visualize and also hear the sound 'ah.' Mix your mind with the sound of 'ah' and then mix the 'ah' sound with the breath in your lungs and mouth. Hold for a moment, and then breathe out slowly and evenly through the mouth while making the sound of 'ahhhhhhh.' The volume of this sound can be soft or loud depending on your surroundings. As you exhale, feel your mind dissolve and with it all thoughts as they are released with your breath out into space. You will feel yourself quieting, but with great clarity of awareness. Repeat this process for several minutes and you will perceive your thoughts as dust motes floating away. This can be practiced anywhere and is remarkable in its ability to calm and rejuvenate the mind. It slows your Mundane Mind so you can recognize that you are greater than its thoughts. You are the Open Sky Mind.

"The third technique is a sky-gazing type of meditation. We do this by gazing into the vast sky. Start by sitting or lying down outside. Close your eyes and begin the mind cooling process. Then with several deep breaths continue on to the 'ah' sound and as you do so, open your eyes and with a soft focus look out into the infinite sky. Your gaze should be on a patch of sky as free as possible from wires, buildings, or trees. DO NOT look at the sun. And hold your gaze with a minimum of blinking. Like your Open Sky Mind, the blue sky is infinite. As you gaze, send the 'ah' breath and with it your smoke-like thoughts out into the sky and into eternal space. Let go of everything that comes up: thoughts of the past and future, emotional dramas, and anything impinging on the senses. Allow everything that freely comes up, to freely go by. Do not become attached to or follow any thought or feeling. Breathe the sky into you, and exhale it out. Continue this process until you become one with the clear sky and boundless space and you'll truly see how your thoughts are only clouds in the vast Open Sky Mind. Then slowly bring yourself back to Earth with the knowledge that the Open Sky is within you and that you are just as vast and infinite.

"This final practice can be done outside during the day or at night under the stars. Try it inside facing a blank wall, or your bedroom ceiling. You can use an empty wall at work, or even your closed eyelids. You'll be surprised at how quickly you will let go of clinging thoughts.

"Persistence in practicing these three is important and you'll find that after a short time your mind and body will have calmed considerably. Then with this inner serenity as your hallmark, and when faced with life's hard choices, peace radiates from this quiet place and gives you the ability to clearly determine which way leads to harmony and bliss.

"One example is to choose kindness over rightness. This choice is impossible if I'm attached to the thought that I must always be right. Another example is before taking any action I ask myself: will this action add to or subtract from the tranquility in my life? The choice is difficult if you don't know what brings you lasting contentment and happiness, or even what those qualities are. Everything in your life comes from the choices you continually make. So I've found, as you will too, that when we clearly see to choose the naturally benevolent path, increased peace flows into our lives.

"Finally, this awareness results in freedom from suffering and the causes of suffering and from this freedom comes life's ultimate natural state and reward, true happiness. It can be yours."

"Whew, that's all for now," Jon ended.

There was a quick round of clapping.

"Copies of tonight's talks are available. Please give your address to Diana." He pointed to me.

I was surprised, but got to meet everyone so I wasn't a stranger any longer.

Later, Jon, Stefan, Jim, and BPM joined me on the floor. Jim and BPM sprawled while Stefan and my teacher sat. These men wanted to hold court with me. Maybe they wanted my hand too. To whom would I give it? Three could woo, but they were too late. My radiance was reserved for only one.

"Did you enjoy our talks?" Stefan's voice boomed in my head.

"Yes, very much." I wanted to hold out my hand for him to kiss.

"What was your favorite part?" Jim asked. He had a sweet smile.

"Being able to let go of unskillful thoughts," I said.

"Unskillful thoughts. Hmm," Stefan said. "She's been listening."

"Yes," Jon said. "I've fed her a lot. I hope she doesn't explode."

"Speaking of eating, I was sorry you left the restaurant that night," Stefan said, "but I want to honor my invitation, so we'll go again."

"Thanks. I usually don't have dinner with strange men, but I'll make an exception."

Then I told them the story of Andrea's hasty escape.

"She's quite a girl," Jim said. "She actually kicked open the window?"

"Yes, she did," I said. "But I still can't believe the chances of running into Stefan again, and here in Safety Harbor. It seems funny."

"Well, Diana, chance favors the person whose mind is prepared," Stefan said, "and someone who acts skillfully. When your mind provides a welcome for chance, you make your own opportunities."

Then Jon confessed.

"Jim and I were the ones meeting Stefan for dinner that evening, but Jim had an unexpected client that delayed us. As we walked from the parking lot, we saw a girl yelling into her phone. We were going to help her when this other more attractive girl came running out. Then you both jumped into a car and sped away before we could do anything but watch."

"That's the first time I saw you, Diana" Jon said, "so you can see how surprised I was when you showed up at the gym. I was waiting by the stairs to talk to you when, all of a sudden, you threw yourself at me. I was flattered, I must say, and I knew then that we were fated to be together."

"I didn't throw myself at you. I tripped or slipped." I hoped I wasn't blushing. More attractive?

"Whichever. It worked. And now here you are with four men admiring you."

"Well, that's quite a little story," I said.

Everyone laughed again. Two patted me on my shoulders. Two patted me on my knees. I did feel admired. But BPM had been silent. Maybe he had nothing to say. Maybe BPM was reserved around other men. I didn't know. But I did know he stared at my breasts the whole time.

Later as Jon and I drove back across the bay to my apartment, frantic thoughts spread through me. Were my clothes and dishes put away? Was the bathroom clean? Was the bed made? My thoughts grew, expanded, and evolved into intimacy.

"You're frowning. Do we need to talk?"

"No." Dilemmas were my friends.

A dilemma involves a choice between two different options that are mutually exclusive. Meaning, if you choose one, you can't have the other. So if I chose to ask, or demand, what I wanted, maybe Jon would be offended and leave. Or if I let him go unspoken, maybe he'd think I wasn't interested and write me off.

"You're uncertain," he said. "I can hear the gears gnashing tough thoughts. You've been thinking about when we get to your place. Let's stop at the drive-in first and get cherry limeades. Then we can talk."

We pulled in and he ordered.

"Go ahead and speak your mind," Jon said. "It's time we discussed things that might get in the way of your learning."

"What learning is that?"

Sometimes when you're with someone special you blurt out anything and everything, many times without thought, and other times you want them to coax it out. But what if that person doesn't know which role they're supposed to play or when they're supposed to play it?

That night, he would have to be the coaxer. I wanted Jon to drag out whatever he had to drag out. I was certain he wanted to hear about my lust for him, about how I would do anything for him, about how he had the key to my heart. But I wasn't saying a thing. Jon would have to pull and pull. I knew that was a silly game, like saying no when you really meant yes, but I felt compelled to play it. It was what I'd been taught, not by him, but by life.

However, that game's fork had sharp tines. First, you never said what you really meant because if they understood you, then they'd get one up on you. Or second, if you spoke your mind openly, you might get rejected—painful. But either way, if you chose to play the game, then afterwards you could relish in all the delicious agonizing and uncertainty. It was a dilemma. My head ached.

"Take my hand," Jon said.

As he clasped my fingers, a lightning bolt of arousal blazed and the car's back seat thundered. I must have fainted or something.

I'm underwater, stuck in the mud. A swaying, green forest of stems surrounds me, their feet unseen below, their heads unseen above.

Then I'm growing—growing upward—upward and away from the clinging ooze. I push through and breathe in purity, breathe in fineness. I breathe in my new life. Then with a pain unlike any other, my head swells, ruptures, and as light washes me, air strokes me, and water shimmers about me, I open my eyes. And, freed from the slime, I ReBecome. I'm a jewel in a flower. I face life and am unafraid.

"I know what you want and I want it too," Jon said softly. "And that time will come, but it will not come tonight." He'd let go of my hand.

As the vision faded, the surface of my emotions glowed with warmth. I finally recognized that Jon was happy to be with me and that he cherished my presence. I saw he was human too and had feelings and desires just as I had, except he understood his. He watched them arise, abide for a while, and then cease. And he didn't cling to them. He knew they would return so he let them go with a natural, unrestrained ecstasy. And when they came back he greeted them with the joy of seeing a well-known friend. I'd never felt so much a part of someone.

I had wanted a quick rendezvous, a hasty coupling so I could put my rope on him. I'd satisfy my needs, stake my claim, and cling. What Jon felt was far beyond that. He desired me, but before he considered his own satisfaction, he wanted me to be strong, to be balanced, to be a person healed from the wounds of life, and to be whole. Without that there was no sense in being together. His kind treatment plus his understanding of what I'd suffered just by living would make a magnificent garden in which to grow our relationship. Only with this could true love bloom.

"Would you like something more to drink?" he asked.

We were still parked at the drive-in, though most of the cars had gone. The colors were vivid.

"No, nothing else, thanks. I'm fine."

Fated to be together!

# Chapter Fifteen:
# A Bear and Some Birds

*"It seems that appreciation and gratitude are always in hindsight."*

"Let me tell you a story," Jon began. "I heard this a long time ago...

"A bear came upon a hunters' camp in the woods and found a large kettle of stew cooking over a fire. The stew smelled wonderful and seeing no one around, he picked up the kettle and tipped it to his mouth. Instantly, the fur on his paws and chest began to singe and stink, and roasting morsels of boiling stew scalded his mouth and tongue. But it tasted so good! Around and around he danced, burned by the kettle, broiled by the stew. He knew he should let go because of the pain and the danger, but he couldn't. Nearby, the hunters smelled the scorching fur and returned to find the bear so engrossed in his dilemma, he didn't see them. He soon became a rug...and the next batch of stew."

"Did you like it?" Jon asked when I didn't say anything. Our heads were together on the pillows.

"The poor bear. But your mention of stew reminds me of my grandmother."

Jon turned his face toward me. "Is she living?"

"No. And I miss her, a lot sometimes. She taught me how to cook while we waited for my mother to come home from work.

And she told me that when you cook to make it good and to always make enough.

"Mother and I moved in with her when we came here from Tennessee, after my father, whom I haven't seen in years, traded my mother, who was forty at the time, for a slim, single twenty. That was the summer before ninth grade and Andrea was the first person to befriend the strange new girl in the neighborhood. Later, she got me dates with her cast-off boyfriends and I was always the smokescreen for her mother when she wanted to go out with college guys. Anyway, my grandmother's beef stew was the best."

"I think she'd be proud of how you turned out," Jon said.

"I hope so. I am starting to like me again." I put my hands behind my head. "And my grandmother would have liked you."

"Did she lecture? Pester you with information and try to wake you up?"

"All the time, and I wish I would have paid more attention to her. But I thought she was ignorant and too old fashioned, and one time I even called her an old fool. She washed my mouth out with soap and I never did it again. But the funny thing is that as I got older I was surprised at everything she had learned."

"It always turns out that way," Jon said. "Hardly anyone appreciates what they have when they have it. We're always looking for a new taste. And then when we reminisce, we miss what we didn't cherish. It seems that appreciation and gratitude are always in hindsight."

"Well, I appreciate being with you," I said as I reached out and tried to stroke his muscled arm.

"And I'm grateful to be here with you too. At the bottom of everything, past the hurts, the fears, and the Mundane Mind, there are only two things, gratitude and service."

"Service?" I saw the grotto man from the shower.

"Service to others," he said. "After you treat others with loving-kindness and compassion, you serve them by bringing happiness into their lives.

"When I was in high school," he recalled, "they gave awards for service to the school and community, but back then I wasn't very impressed with all the acclaim for helping others. Later on, I found out I was wrong and that if you only take, you get plugged up and have a constipated life. Giving in proportion to what you receive keeps good things coming your way. Besides, it's a reward in itself to see someone's eyes light up when you do a kind deed. You might say that seems a little selfish, but soon you focus on the rewards you give, not receive. Now, I even give friends presents on my birthday."

His voice sounded sleepy. "Tell me more about your grandmother."

"Well, her kumquat and seagrape jellies always sold out at the church bazaars. And she adored nature, and told me to always leave the smallest footprint."

"The smallest footprint?"

"It's the saying you see in parks, "Leave Only Footprints!" She said that if you leave the smallest footprint on your world and on the people in your life, then anytime you look back you won't have regrets and no guilt or shame.

"And she always told me to recognize beauty and to walk in it. She wanted that for our community too and calmly tried to convince our neighbors' consciences. But their wallets wouldn't listen and even though she sometimes felt powerless, she just kept trying."

"She sounds like she was ahead of her time," Jon said.

"Yes. And I know sometimes she got stressed," I said, and rolled my head, bumping his.

"Please remember," Jon said, "that stress is only the friction caused when your fear of losing something you think you have or of not getting something you think you deserve, rubs against reality. Those same fears also fuel anger. So when they arise in your mind, be aware of them, and let them go. Positive mental and emotional states reduce stress. Others can be stressed-out if they want, but you can choose to be calm."

"That's what I choose for sure. Now tell me something I don't know."

"What do you want to know?"

Tell me how you feel about me, I wanted to say. Or, are my breasts large enough? But instead I said, "Something nobody else knows."

"Well, let's see…I'm descended from Pocahontas and, according to my mother, also Blackbeard the pirate."

"Hmm. What else?"

"I grew up in an island swamp. I've lived in a cave. I've been a gardener, a mailman, a teenage bootlegger, and I've worked on a pig farm. Is that enough?"

"No, more. Please."

"Well, I have a feather collection, the only things left on the beach after the tourists go home, and a matchbook set, but I don't smoke." He thought for a moment. "I hate tomato aspic, but love key lime pie. I've been in two car wrecks and two boat wrecks, and after being in a helicopter crash I don't fly—ever. I've been shot, and once I was stabbed by a woman stuck in her Mundane Mind."

"Shot! Stabbed!" A shock wave of surprise and fear thrilled me.

"Yes, Diana, and I still have the scars. But we'll talk about those another time.

"Anyway, I'm a citizen of Earth, and all the atoms of my body came from a supernova billions of years ago."

"That's nice, but tell me something more about…" Then I sensed a shift in his energy and quickly decided not to get too personal right now. Later, I'd rub his lats and rhomboids. That would loosen him up and then, being so relaxed, maybe he'd share every secret. "…your island home."

\*

"The sand that sifted between my toes was as white as milk," he began, "and as it reflected the blinding stare of the sun, it burned me even under a beach umbrella.

"Then at twilight, below iridescent evening storms, the deepening blues exposed unique tints of water and my fantasies would fly through those colorful skies.

"There were a lot fewer people then. Mangroves grew from the water and pine trees swayed on the land. There was swamp everywhere and out of the swamp came roaches as big as mice, mice as big as rats, and rats as big as gulls, although they were a different color. Raccoons peeped from pepper trees and snakes slithered through thickets. There was dense jungle and even quicksand. My sister rode her bike into it once. We hooted at her, but it could have been serious.

"I can still see mother and *my* grandmother sitting on the old pier on a Friday night. We'd walk out there to escape the mosquitoes. Each one wanted only a small bite, but because there were so many, we would have soon been drained. We would eat and visit. I was so tired of seafood that once for my birthday I told my mother: no more lobster. I wanted a hamburger. I wanted what I thought was a normal life. And that was my first lesson in how the mind had tricked me into believing that just because I didn't have the same things others had, I should be unhappy.

"At night with the stars and moon overhead, the distant lights of the mainland would call siren-like, promising me a happier existence. It took a long time for their allure to burn out, but I finally saw I had everything I needed right where I was sitting on that dock in the bay. All happiness and all suffering were inside me, and I had the choice which to experience.

"Hurricanes would come and go, but we weren't swept away. We rebuilt."

✳

"Is that enough," he asked.

"Just a little more, please."

Jon hesitated. "All right. Maybe you would be interested in this part."

"When I was young," he said, "late one Saturday night at a bonfire on the north point of the island, I had an awakening that helped shape my future life.

"I think a flash of awareness can be more enlightening than a lot of experience. All the training, all the teachers, all the reading and study I've done was only to help me comprehend that event. I've made a lot of misguided and unnecessary detours, but I've always come back to that one moment."

"What did you see?"

"I saw that the core of life is happiness. I know when it's said aloud it doesn't seem like much, but it is.

"And I understood that throughout history and even before, everyone had sought the same thing: everyone had felt separated from happiness and they all desperately wanted to reconnect with it."

The figure from the rock wall of my dental dream drummed to me.

"Our entire lives," he continued, "everything we say, everything we do, everything we buy, and everyone we love, are only attempts to regain the happiness we think is missing. And when we find it, we grasp. Then as changes come and clinging has to end, the suffering is terrible."

I didn't like the last part, but I understood.

Jon went on, "I also realized that though the things that stimulate our happiness may be individual, the feeling within each one of us is identical and even when happiness seems to have left, it hasn't gone anywhere. And I knew that if happiness wasn't already inside of me, I wouldn't be able to recognize it when I received it from the outside. It was the core of my being.

"But as I watched others, I found that for many life was a burden and a time to be endured. It was then I understood what Sophocles had said, 'our happiness depends on wisdom all the way.'"

"Maybe they don't know," I said.

"Perhaps," he said. "But Diana, I want you to understand that suffering isn't the core. It's only a dirty blanket that can be kicked off if you want it off. Happiness is the essence for everyone and those who don't see this haven't taken the time to look."

"So how do you kick off this filthy blanket?" I'd fanned my hair across the pillow, wanting to look wanton.

"My insight showed me that the blanket is woven of fear. Anger stains its threads and it has tears of sadness. Ragged holes may allow glimpses of joy, but mostly it smothers."

"Fear, with blotches of anger?"

"Yes. The same fears that are the sources of stress I mentioned earlier: fear of losing the things we think we have, or fear of not getting the things we think we deserve. Now, I know that if I boil them down, I find those fears are only things temporarily hidden or temporarily misunderstood. And when I understand that, I can take relief-giving action."

"What kind of action?" Some of my hair was covering my eyes and I watched him through it.

"I stare fear in the face and see if it's real. Most fears are nebulous and blow away. I get information because knowledge kills fear. Then I take action by turning fear energy outward. I cultivate generosity, loving-kindness, and I help others. And as I redirect, the filthy blanket dissolves, the anger rinses away, and my core shines through.

"When I say, 'I'm too busy,' that's just fear talking. It doesn't want to lose its existence. And, I must remember, I am not my thoughts. With skillful actions, fear and anger wither. As Stefan said about the mind, wrapped in fear, it becomes my master, not my helper. I can change that.

"Also, fear keeps me inadequate. So when you hear there's nothing to fear but fear itself, it's really true. So let me give you a homily or two to add to those of your grandmother. Fear: False Events Appear Real. Or, Face Everything And Rejoice."

As Jon finished, I was reminded of a boyfriend who had belittled me. I'd stayed with him because I didn't want to be alone. But if I'd faced my fear of loneliness, seen it had no power for harm and gotten rid of him fast, recovery from his anger wouldn't have taken months. But today, I didn't want to think about that. I gently rubbed my shoulder against his.

"What was the moral of the story about the bear and the stew?"

"The moral was that the bear held onto the hot kettle because he thought the taste of the stew outweighed any consequences. We all hold onto possessions, people, or ideas that are burning us. We cling until the unpleasant consequences come to see us. Then we cry and complain loudly when we end up as rugs and we can't imagine what happened."

With his words came a loud burst of sounds and a wild flurry of wings.

I sat up with a start. "What's going on?"

"It's just the black grackles chatting with the sunset, but in their joyous abandon they might not notice us here below them. And remember, earlier we saw them pecking at fish heads."

To punctuate his observation, I heard a warning plop.

We picked up our blankets and pillows, grabbed the picnic basket, and admired the setting sun over the lake as we walked to Jon's car.

# Chapter Sixteen: Swimming Ahead

*"We're experienced, roughened by our lives. We have to prove we're steady swimmers. This is the way of life."*

"*You* look terrific!"

Pleased Jon had noticed, I pirouetted. "All my hard work is working."

My clothes were looser. I'd lost inches and I was sure they were in places that counted. A boyfriend once said women were like bathtubs because they filled from the bottom up and emptied from the top down. But I was different. My loss was in the middle.

"Let's take measurements again so we can chart your progress," Jon said.

He seemed distant. At first I thought it was me, but it must have been something else. Wait. Maybe it had been me. Maybe I hadn't been appreciative of his compliment.

I thought back to that same boyfriend. One evening before dinner I complimented him on his appearance. I had a hidden motive. I wanted him to spend the night so he would stay. To my surprise, he spewed anger, not thanks. "Do you mean there was something wrong with me, that I wasn't attractive to you before tonight?" His tone created a verbal chopstick war at the Thai restaurant. And later I had the proverbial headache.

"Let's take the measurements," Jon repeated.

"Fine." I didn't dig, I weighed.

"Did you know that if you don't perform muscle-strengthening exercises you lose lean body mass even if your weight never changes?"

"No," I said with concern. "How does that happen?"

"I'll give you an example," he said. "A 140-pound woman at age 30 might have a fat percentage of 20%. This equals 28 pounds of fat and 112 pounds of lean body weight. When she reaches 50 with the same 140 pounds, but having done nothing to build or retain muscle, her fat percentage might now be 30%, or more. At 30% this equals 42 pounds of fat and 98 pounds of lean body weight. Over the 20-year period she had converted 14 pounds of lean to fat. That conversion is a natural process with aging and can only be countered by muscle-strengthening exercise plus a healthy diet."

"I'm glad my numbers are headed in the right direction," I said as we finished.

"I am too. Let's get started."

Tonight was chest and triceps night, again.

"She's got good form." It was BPM. He tried to smile, but looked unhappy.

"True," Jon said. "Because without good form, workouts are a waste. But Jack, we're busy. What do you need?"

"Nothing. I was steamed, but I'm calmer now."

"What happened?" I wanted a longer rest.

"Somebody scratched my new truck on purpose! They keyed it! On the driver's door!" The muscles in his jaw pulsed and he flexed his hands and wrists. "Now why would someone do that? I parked way out in the lot and it wasn't hurting anyone."

Maybe the truck wasn't hurting, but BPM was.

"Who does things like that?" he continued and shook his head. "I worked hard to buy that truck and now it's scratched."

"I know you did, Jack," Jon said, "and I was pleased it was the one you'd been waiting for. It was a reward for all your efforts and I'm sorry that it's damaged. It makes you mad when someone deliberately does something that could have been avoided."

"But why do people do those things?" I asked.

"You can answer that yourself."

"Because they get a momentary bit of pleasure."

"That's correct."

"Explain it to me," BPM said, looking at Jon.

"Think what was going through the mind of the person who scratched your truck. They saw it and recognized it as something of value. Then they developed feelings of dissatisfaction and envy, and formed the intention to damage it. Next they keyed it. And finally, they felt some pleasure about what they'd done.

"This was a person who feels both powerless and very dissatisfied with their life. In striking anonymously they wanted relief from their almost continuous suffering and they succeeded, but only for a moment. Immediately their unhappiness returned with this new unskillful action added and their downward spiral continued. They were dispirited and so they pushed their affliction onto you, but they accomplished nothing and only made themselves even more unhappy."

"But what can I do?" BPM asked.

"Until they become aware of their discontent, very little can be done. It takes willingness and discipline for a person to look at how much they're suffering inside. Many people spend their lives feeling poorly about themselves or blaming others rather than use that same time to improve. But eventually some get to where they are hurting so much, they decide it must stop. It's usually triggered by an unpleasant event that affects *them*. Then they awaken to their anguished condition. And when this occurs, they stop adding to their burden of unskillful acts.

"There's another certainty," Jon added. "At some point the results of their misdeeds will return to see them when they least expect it."

"I hope so," BPM said. "If I knew who they were, I'd go check out their car."

"No, Jack. Let those thoughts go. They hurt only you and might lead you to do something you'd regret. Just get your truck fixed."

"Okay. Talk to you later." And with a half-wave, BPM left.

"Sorry about the interruption," Jon said. "He got more than he intended. And he has his eye on you."

"He can forget it. He doesn't interest me."

"Well, what kind of man does interest you, Diana?"

My first impulse was to scream "YOU DO!" But it was complicated. "It's changing," I said. "I thought I knew, but I think I was hooked on stereotypes and now I'm not sure anymore."

"That's all right. We all can get overwhelmed by culture, some more than others."

"I've been thinking," I said. "You give so much to me, what do you want?"

"I want you to be happy."

"That's all?" Please, that can't be all.

"No…it isn't. But when you have that, you'll have everything. And…"

"Hello! Hi there!" Irene strode over to us.

Darn! I couldn't get a word in edgewise.

"You look different," she observed. "He really is a good trainer, but if you get tired of him, come see me. I'll work with you."

This drew a false frown from Jon, but his eyes laughed.

"Thanks, Irene. But she has lots of lessons to go."

Irene smiled and walked away.

"Back to what you were saying…" I began.

"Let's finish your triceps exercises, then we can talk…about personal things."

Rats! Seagull-sized rats!

Hell, I've heard some say, is repetition. So when you're training, doing exercise after exercise, set after set, you'll use anything you see or can think of to relieve your immediate discomfort and distract your mind. A woman's angry face caught my eye while I was using the Triceps Pull Down.

"How does a person get that way?" I asked Jon as the glowering woman dragged past staring at the floor.

"Remember, it's important not to judge or compare based solely on someone's outsides, but it appears she spews bile, not nectar."

"So she's full of vinegar?"

"Yes," Jon said. "When you get run down you develop a low opinion about life. As this attitude becomes ingrained, you become less resilient and unpleasant things or events are drawn to you like jackals. Then they chew you to pieces.

"When you're exhausted you don't have the strength to counter troubles. Then even human animals sense your weaknesses and your willingness to comply. Kinder individuals understand; others look for an advantage. And once you're compromised, you have to find a new pack. But if you haven't rebuilt your weakened condition, fresh jackals begin circling again—immediately.

"This is why geographic cures never work. When you move someplace new, your unresolved problems are the first to arrive."

That had certainly been true when mother and I moved to Tampa. But finally we, meaning I, were finished and I saw Jon glance at the gym's front door with a concerned expression. The blond woman he knew was standing by the desk and looking our way.

As I stared back I felt like maybe he wanted to be with her, and maybe only her. Period. Then there'd never be time for coffee and conversation. Never any time for *me*. He'd said he had other female clients, but I didn't want to see or know about them. I wished her into oblivion, or at least out the door.

But by this time I should have known. Some men were inattentive, asleep. They were wrapped up in themselves, sports, or some babe. Their minds tracked their eyes and both jumped around like the drunken monkeys I'd heard about. Not my teacher. When Jon was with you, he focused on you alone. This was both good and bad. Good—you were special, the center of his world. Bad—it was impossible to hide anything, or to lie.

"If I've been distracted," Jon said, "it's because I've been thinking about her. Her name is Corinne and she has special needs."

"What needs?" I heard hissing.

"If she's agreeable, I'll ask her to tell you her story."

"I don't *care* about her story." And, I almost added, I only care about you.

"You might. I'll ask anyway. Would you like to meet her?"

"Not tonight. I'm tired."

"Suit yourself. But I want to leave you with a thought, Diana.

"Jealousy is rage powered by the fear-fueled greed of possession. We've talked about attachment, so you see how this applies. Trust is a razor's edge, you either trust or you don't. If you do, distrust will ruin it. If you don't, mistrust won't fix it. With jealousy all your attention is focused inward toward what you want and not focused outward toward being loving and kind. It is truly a form of suffering. But when your powerlessness flows away so does jealousy.

"Anyway, you've finished," Jon ended. "Why not sit in the sauna? You can relax and let go of your thoughts. You've earned it; you pumped hard." With one last smile, he walked away—*to her.*

I pinned back my hair and put on my shower shoes. Then as I closed my locker a woman came right over next to me and slipped. She grabbed me and we both toppled. I got a tile floor close-up and saw a few curly hairs.

I sat up and recognized the darker blond woman who'd been sitting with her friend in front of my locker. It'd been a while and I hadn't thought anymore about them.

"Oh...sorry. I have to thank you for Kristi," she gushed.

"Kristi?"

"You know, the woman who asked about the spot on her face." When I looked confused, she said, "You told her to get it checked. You told her right before your nude-with-a-towel scene. The doctor told her it was serious, removed it, and said that had she delayed any longer it would have been much worse. She won't go out until it heals, but told me to say thanks if I saw you."

"Tell her, 'You're welcome.' Now let's get up. People might get the wrong idea."

She left and I actually smiled because before I wouldn't have been so honest. I would have said something like that's your problem and you deal with it. Now I was pleased I'd spoken up.

In the wet sauna, I spread my towel on the tile bench and sat. Drops ran down the wall and the air was thick with steam and smelled of men. The glass door was a blurred rectangle of light. With a click and a hiss the steam-generator in the far corner came on and only for a moment, I closed my eyes.

Seaweed weavings soften the sun's rays, before, at an unfathomable depth, they go dark. Bits of white spiral down until lost in the deep blue below.

A crab or two and a clutch of lobsters scurry as I approach, glide, and leave them behind. Anemones duck.

Day dissolves, the water dims, flashes with color, fades into blackness. The ceiling, now clear, reveals the white curve of a shell. Pale green waves illuminate my path.

With light, the silvery roof returns. I smell my destination and as the day ripens, I arrive.

A pod circles and spirals before large holes in a reef. Some swimmers show their undersides to the coral as they glide. I've arrived late. The dance has already begun.

I join and swim discreetly. And not wanting to tire, I wait. But the water's smell is strong and restraint is difficult.

At last! Mates squirt from the holes and our motions become frantic.

The pretty ones are chosen first. Maybe they're smoother, maybe more attractive with refined noses and undamaged fins, but the pretty ones go first. And I wished I were one. Chosen for their skin, they never develop skills to form a lasting bond. They swim off after satisfaction. But they're here every time and always win.

Those remaining after the first choices have a tough time. We're experienced, roughened by our lives. We've scrapes, cuts. We're solid, but lacking prettiness makes our work hard. We have to show we have loyalty and dependability. We have to prove we're steady swimmers. This is the way of life.

But there are never enough mates and there are more seekers every time. Some will leave alone, no partner for the rocks. But not me.

# Chapter Sixteen: Swimming Ahead

After swimming in skillful patterns, someone attractive approaches and my heart warms. My fins twitch in appreciation. But many holes are taken so we must dive deeper.

Gliding and rubbing, we don't see another, unhappy at being denied, following stealthily.

As we arrive at an empty cave, anticipation floods me. But as I hurry to follow inside, I'm seized by the tail and pulled into open water. My side splits on the ragged rocks, and I see a familiar face. Rows of shiny white teeth grimace at me. Then I'm bitten, torn, and a fin ripped loose. I see a flicker of tail enter the cave as I sink, my air and anticipation bubbling away. I scrape against the coral.

I felt a squeeze on my knee. A voice said, "Wake up now." I opened my eyes a slit—and started in surprise. It was a mocha mountain seen through fog. The mountain undulated and the mists swirled. Above craggy cliffs, the top was black. A mental picture: mountains were white on top, not black. Long ridges sloped toward me and the peak rose and fell. I was very tired, I thought. I closed my eyes.

Again came the gentle shake, but now it was my other knee. Again the voice, "You're getting too hot."

Yes! I was hot all right! I could feel the fire in my belly. Want, want, want! I didn't open my eyes.

Then, thunder and earthquake: "Wake up NOW!" The shaking grew violent and my eyes flew open. The mountain ridges reached to my shoulders.

Out of the mists came the face of Oscar, sweat streaming down his cheeks. "Are you okay? Don't go to sleep in here! You can get overheated which isn't good. Stay awake."

"I wasn't asleep!" I did not know what I had been.

"Sorry. I thought you were out. You were moaning and jerking. Maybe a bad workout dream. Sometimes I have gym-mares of being buried under tons of weights. It can be scary. I had to wake you up."

"That's fine," I said, calming. "Maybe I dozed off. I had an exhausting session." This reply eased Oscar. I hadn't meant to bark. He was only being kind.

"Thanks. I appreciate your concern." I put a smile in my voice.

He went to his corner. "I want to apologize to you," came the steamy reply. "I was tired when I last saw you and forgot you were sitting there. So I let it rip. Too many protein drinks. Gives me gas. You left fast. Sorry."

"That's okay. It happens." I'd forgotten about the hellaceous stench.

"When you meet my mother, please don't tell her," he said. "She taught me manners and would be disappointed. I'm not always so thoughtless."

"I won't tell. I promise." *When*?

"You should go out now. You came in thirty minutes ago and, after I shaved and showered, I followed to apologize." I couldn't see his face.

"Okay. I'll go." Only thirty minutes? I staggered through the heated haze and out.

As I sat and dangled my legs in the pool's cool waters, its edge was rough against my fins.

# Chapter Seventeen:
# Sensing Me, Sensing You

*"My friends, it is neither the wind nor the pole that causes the flag to flap. It is your minds that flap."*

My shaded eyes filled with knights as dust whirlers blew horse smells into my nose. Dressed in colorful armor, red, yellow, green, and black knights stood next to stamping horses ready to carry them to meet any challenge to their lady's honor.

Then trumpeters announced the beginning of the competition, and wearing plumed helmets and waving colored scarves, the knights mounted and paraded in front of the expectant crowd.

Pennants snapped and a multitude filled the stands: some dressed in elaborate costumes and others were more casual, some covered up and others exposed more, some had come far and others brought offspring. Sounds rose and fell in the breeze.

Earlier, I'd gotten a splinter from the banister, but was now seated comfortably and ready for Merlin to cast his spell. I placed my greasy palm on Jon's hand and told him how much I'd enjoyed myself.

"A person is born to enjoy life," he responded. "We've talked about the usual five senses: sight, smell, sound, taste, and touch. But in addition, the mind also senses. If you don't believe me see what happens in your mind and in your body when you think about a memory or a hot fantasy. You know that reaction. If the mind didn't sense, there'd be nothing. Have you ever given yourself a headache by just thinking? Similar to how a sight, smell, sound, taste, or touch can evoke a reaction, so can a thought."

I squeezed his hand. He'd been looking over the crowd, but I wanted him to look at me and not at scantily clad wenches.

"The result of a precious human birth is that a person possesses those six senses," Jon continued. "And how wonderful they are! Without them, our only contact with the world, we're nothing. Now you may say, 'Everybody knows that.' But do they? When your senses contact something, be it a person, place, thing, or thought, one of only three simple feelings arises which are pleasure, displeasure, and neutral. All others are derived from these three. To illustrate, imagine a $1000 dollar bill, a horse dropping, and a block of wood. Using your senses you feel pleasure about the $1000 dollar bill, displeasure about the horse dropping, and neutral about the block of wood. And from these three reactions you build stories. Yet all three are only plant materials. This example is simple, but your entire life is run from those reactions of your senses.

"Does that help?" he ended.

"Uh, huh." It was hard to answer while gnawing on a buttered ear.

"Does my lady wish a joust for her honor?" The red knight leaned toward me from his red-draped horse. The shiny helmet hid his face. I'd seen him ride in front of the crowd and was surprised he'd chosen me to champion.

"Uh, huh." I nodded. Corn juice ran down my chin. I rubbed it off with my fingers. I wanted to lick them, but ladies didn't do that. So I wiped them on what I thought was my napkin, but turned out to be the bottom of my shirt.

The red and yellow knights faced each other from opposite ends of the jousting field. And with a blare of trumpets, they hurtled toward each other. Midway they met with a thunk. Neither was unseated. They repeated and on the third pass the yellow knight unhorsed the red knight, who landed in the dirt.

I clapped my buttery palms together. "So much for my honor!"

"So it would seem," Jon said. "He tried hard though."

"Serves him right. He should have tried even harder. After all I'm worth it," I said with mock indignation

"That you are. And is there anything else my lady desires?"

Two knights, the green knight and the yellow one again, lined up. The red knight was gone. My honor had been forgotten in the hazy afternoon heat.

"No, nothing. And thank you. You've been a gentleman all day." I used my oily-salty fingers to count his contributions. "One, you said how lovely I looked when you picked me up on time; two, you drove us to this medieval faire and didn't get angry when we got turned around; three, you didn't mind when sand blew into our eyes; four, you haven't complained about the crowds; five, you treated me to an exciting elephant ride; and six, you've bought whatever I wanted to eat or drink. You've treated me like a princess and I love you for it."

OOPS! I hadn't meant for that last to slip out, but...there it was. In that context it sounded harmless. I waited for his reply. It would either be thanks, or the whip. I hoped for thanks. I didn't think I'd get the whip. I got neither.

He simply placed my hand on his arm and led us along the seats until we stepped down. Then we went to the nearest refreshment booth where he purchased two drinks to wash the dust from our throats. As I looked back, the crowd roared its approval as the yellow knight was knocked to the ground.

"There's a play in the amphitheater that starts in a few minutes," I said as I snaked my arm through his. "Let's go see it."

"Okay," he agreed, and allowed himself to be steered into the playhouse.

We sat on a bench with a good view of the stage. The aisles were ankle deep in abandoned food pieces and assorted debris. When the sun reached into this area later, the smell would be unbearable. I crunched a turkey leg bone under my heel.

The forty-five-minute play was about misunderstandings. Everyone thought a certain someone had done something dumb, I mean unskillful, when it was really a different someone who'd done it. The slapstick antics would have had people rolling in the aisles, were they not full of trash. It wasn't too off color, but the innuendos left little to the imagination. This brought lots of knowing laughs. I enjoyed it and thought my teacher did too.

We exited with the boisterous crowd and sat on a shaded bench in a flagpole-bordered pavilion. Loud pops came from the snapping flags and there was a lot of motion. When I squinted upward I could see a colorful umbrella on one flag and an intricate banner on another. The others were waving too wildly to see their designs.

"Those flags remind me of a story," Jon said.

We hadn't spoken much in the theater so it was good to have him back with me.

"Two men were watching a flag flapping at the top of a tall pole and debating. The first man said, 'It's being attached to the pole that causes the flag to flap.' 'No,' said the second man, 'it's the wind moving past the pole that makes the flag flap.' 'That's not right,' said the first man. 'If the flag wasn't attached to the pole, then it wouldn't flap.' 'That's not right either,' said the second man. 'Without the wind the flag wouldn't flap.'

"This discussion went on for some time. At last a learned man came past and the two arguing men decided to let him determine the correct answer to their debate. After a moment's thought he responded, 'My friends, it is neither the wind nor the pole that causes the flag to flap. It is your minds that flap.'"

I was perplexed. I didn't see how the story applied and said so.

"That's all right. I was telling the story more to myself than to you."

"I'm not sure what you mean. I was listening. 'It's your mind that flaps,'" I summarized.

"Of course you were listening. What I meant was I told the story to remind myself of my own flapping mind. It usually flaps over some desire."

"What does it want?" Maybe he had heard me.

"It wants to apologize for the interruption during the jousting match. It starts to flap and unless I keep an eye on it, it engages my mouth and off we go. I really don't want to get too carried away explaining, but I keep thinking that if you'll bear with me a little you'll learn what you need to know to smooth your course. But for now let's shop and give my mind something to occupy it."

"Great," I said. "Shopping is as much fun as jousting. But before we go, let me say that I'm not offended when you want to teach me. I value our times together. And thank you for caring. In the past, men have lectured or raved at me with no thought as to what I felt, so this is a pleasant change."

"Good. But if I get carried away again, Diana, please tell me."

"I will. But I heard you about the six senses and won't forget."

Soon we encountered a shop selling incense and scented oils. The smells were a delightful mix and until then I'd never understood the excitement about aroma therapy. According to Andrea, scent was for attracting men, but I could smell that it went beyond that simple notion.

I decided to buy three small bottles of frankincense, lavender, and ylang-ylang mixed with nutmeg and orange. Accompanied by twitching black eyebrows, the sales wench told me I had to buy the last one if I wanted to be successful in my endeavors with the gentleman accompanying me.

"The frankincense will add an air of exoticness to your bedroom," she explained in a low voice. "Then the lavender will relax him and the three-part blend dabbed on your neck, or wherever, will seduce him. He won't have a chance."

I hoped she was right because the Persuader sample had been a dud. I slipped the bottles into my purse.

"Would you like a candle," I asked when I joined him on the other side of the store. "Pick the one that reminds you the most of me."

"No, not today. Besides I think of you too much anyway."

Well, that was good, but I didn't ask him to explain.

We continued on and passed a booth filled with heavy medieval furniture, too unshapely for comfort. Then we discovered a shop where fountains bubbled and chimes rang. We let our ears explore.

"Here. I'll get these for you to wear to work," Jon said as he handed me a set of silver ankle bells.

"No. Not there! But because you selected them," I said, "I'm going to buy them." I could think of better places to wear those little bells. "You can take me to dinner instead at that restaurant we found while we were wandering."

"We were evaluating alternate routes," Jon said. "And dinner will be my pleasure, my lady, but you must wear your bells or you will have to serve."

"No problem, sir! But I can't dine in my greasy shirt so let's visit the clothing store under the side-by-side oaks first."

Hanging garments shaded most of the windows so it was shadowy inside and I heard soft music playing on medieval instruments. The saleswoman was regally dressed in an eggplant color I'd heard called aubergine, had dark kohl-lined eyes, and smelled faintly of musk.

"Is there anything in particular Milady is looking for?" she purred. Her velvety voice suited her.

"A nice dress for dinner. Something for a gentleman's viewing."

"Let's see if we have your size," she said, giving me a quick head-to-toe review.

"Your gentleman appears conservative," she said as she looked at Jon watching the crowd outside, "but underneath he's a tiger."

"How do you know?"

"You see how relaxed he's sitting? His breathing is slow; his fires are banked. But he's alert, especially to you, and he's ready to take action in a single moment. And I bet when he looks at you, I mean when he really looks at you with his penetrating eyes, you about pee your pants."

Hmm. Yes.

Then she fluttered about and gathered an armful of dresses from which I selected one that was dark blue, smooth against my skin, and wasn't too clingy.

Through a low doorway I glimpsed a small men's section. Most of the clothes were a puffy medieval style. But there was a narrow rack of men's tights. I loved the way they felt as I rubbed them between my fingers.

"Would you like me to ask the gentleman to try those on for you?" The proprietress peeked through the doorway.

"No...I don't think so," I stammered as I continued to rub the fabric.

"I'll say it was my idea."

"No. But thanks."

"I'll tell you what," she said. "Those haven't been selling well so I'll just stick one in your bag. It'll be our secret."

Moments later in the scattered sunshine under the trees, Jon asked, "What did you want me to try on?" He had been attentive!

"Oh, nothing."

"Next time show me what you like. I might be interested." He shrugged his shoulders as we walked on.

A colorful knave peddling candies under a blue and white awning waved us over. He bowed and offered me a sticky sample.

"Wow! These are great and so creamy. You have to have one."

"All right, but only one," Jon said. "I love chocolate, but if I eat it late in the day, I don't sleep well at night."

"Gosh. That's too bad," I said as I rolled the flavors around on my tongue.

"At one time," he said, "I used caffeine to boost my spirits, but I always needed more to re-lift them. Now I take in as little as possible, including chocolate."

"That's nice. But I'm eating this," I said as I licked my fingers discreetly. I wasn't ready to give up caffeine, especially chocolate.

Later on our way to the silk shop, we passed a booth selling carvings made from exotic wood or banded stone.

"Do you like the feel of the wood?" Jon asked as he handed me an intricate carved bear standing on its hind legs.

"The grain is beautiful and smooth to the touch." I saw him displaying it in his home and telling his friends we'd selected it together.

"Do you ship?" he asked the counter man, whose face dripped a long white, fake beard. The whiskers twitched side to side.

"Ship?" I was surprised. "We can take it with us so you can enjoy it later."

"It isn't for me. It's for a former student because she deserves a gift."

"She graduated?"

"There's no graduation," Jon laughed. "But she regained enough awareness and knowledge to make positive changes in her life's direction. And those took her to a different part of the country where her physical location is in line with her mental direction. You may do the same one day."

"I don't want to go anywhere," I said, alarmed. "I'm in no hurry to make that kind of change."

"Well, maybe not now. But you still have to become friends with change, Diana. It will always be your constant companion, and is the true definition of time."

Inside the silk store I could hear the elephants in the distance as I let my fingers stray. Silk was so sensuous to feel and so beautiful to behold. I could enhance its mild smell with the exotic oils. And then with seductive music to titillate his ears, silver bells to encircle both ankles, vivid eyes and passionate lips, I saw a vision of what I could do to him and for him and...I found the kohl-eyed saleswoman was right.

"Do you have a restroom?" I quizzed the clerk, and then hurried.

When I returned, a maroon silk skirt and a beaded silk vest called to me, but they were expensive and not sensible.

"Go try them on." The smiling sales girl was dressed in layers of multi-colored silk to match the medieval theme. She pointed.

The changing room was so tiny I could hardly turn around. I shimmied out of my clothes while bumping into the walls so many times they threatened to collapse.

Finally I was dressed in the silk and had to reconsider my plan of modeling for Jon. As long as I stood still or didn't sit down I was fine, but anything else and it was show time with little left to the imagination. But the touch of silk on my skin was erotic and made me feel brazen. The thought of dancing for him while dressed like this made me dizzy. I leaned against the flimsy plywood and the walls disappeared.

Startled awake, my widely spread legs ache from the ceaseless rocking. I squeeze my knees together, but they won't move so I give up and try to regain my sleep. It is impossible. Bumping jolts run from hip to head and with the swaying they threaten to unseat my hastily eaten, gristly dinner. I moan.

Swinging his head around at my sound and with moonlight reflecting off large box-shaped teeth that smile at me from between wet, ropey lips, a stinking bray blasts my ears.

"Shhh. Shhh. We must be quiet. There is much night left." I pat his brown hairy hump. We do not stop.

After leaving Lou-lan, we had avoided the place from which nothing living returns and entered the mountains.

We are as quiet in the cold air as we can be with only a soft bell on the lead camel and one on the last. Sounds run up the rocks like shaggy goats and proclaim our presence to all. This time we are not giving lives or cargo in tribute; this time I am not bending over to insure our safe passage. Smells from the spices packed behind me mingle with rock and camel scents, and as I grip tightly with my thighs, I feel the coarse blanket under my maroon silk pants. I shiver.

Around us, the treeless peaks are black with night. Tilting my head back I see their white teeth against the dotted sky. Lurking between two of the tallest are the guardian of the night and her new consort, the hairy-tailed one. Together they appear as two eyes watching, with one eye winking. And what secret does she share with her wink, I wonder? I wish the trick on another.

Listening beyond the tinkling bells, I hear them. Again. I had been told it was only the wind whispering with the stones, but I know the truth. Many had passed into these mountains and many had passed on before leaving. Some naturally, others not. I hear their cries, their calls to us to stop and give them warmth to cling to. Gazing about, I see ghostly riders, vaporous caravans proceeding through the night sky on their way to nowhere. I do not know which is worse—the heated riders of the day, or these chill specters of the night. I begin to weep.

The walls abruptly rematerialized returning my life to within its limits. I wiped my watery eyes with the vest, then quickly changed and left the dressing room.

"I'm not getting them today," I said to Jon, my breath coming in catches. "I'll take one of their cards."

"I'm sure they looked nice," he said with maybe a hint of disappointment. "If it's cost I can help."

"No. It's not that," I said, a little calmer. "They aren't what I want right now."

"Okay. Then let's have dinner. I'm hungry for some real food." He patted his six-pack for emphasis.

When we arrived at the rustic restaurant located in an old home, there were only a few cars parked under the large banyan trees out front. Inside, the dining room was dark with a smoky smell and the wooden floor was covered in places by red and black rugs. Our table was made to hold the weight of a lot of food, its scarred surface having served many diners.

The current specialty was medieval fare so we ordered thick bean soup, crusty black bread with a crock of spiced butter, and mulled cider.

As I placed the cloth napkin on the lap of my new dress, I heard my ankle bells tinkle unseen.

Later, on the way home I dozed. The ride was smoother than elephants—or camels.

# Chapter Eighteen:
# Remembering the Ramp

*"Don't compare your insides with their outsides."*

"*Let's* keep in touch!" I've heard that so many times and then never heard again. But with Andrea that usually wasn't the case, except when she had a new boyfriend. "Something must be wrong," I said aloud as I reached for the phone to call her again—and it rang.

It was Andrea, the psychic.

"Diana, can you meet me at Four Palms right away?" she asked, although it was more of an order than a request. Andrea was like that sometimes.

"That'll be fine." It was Saturday again. Friday night's workout had been exhausting. I'd slept soundly so that morning I felt charitable. I knew the urgency had to do with her love life so maybe she'd have a good story.

I ate a meal replacement bar for breakfast and then I was off.

I waved in at the front desk, dumped my bag in locker No. 55, and went to the cardio area to await Miss Andrea.

On my way I noticed BPM using the Chest Press machine. When he saw me, he pumped out his pecs, flexed his arms, and performed a provocative weight lifter's pose. I was amused, but took a detour to avoid an encounter.

Irene soon joined me.

"Are you having a good day, Diana?"

"Yes, so far," I said as I looked around. "Do you see what bicycle pants man is doing? He's quite a character."

"That he is," Irene said. Then lowering her voice, "But he has a secret not many people know."

I've never been one for gossiping since I was the subject of a lot of it in high school, but… "What is it?"

She motioned to follow her up the stairs and to the back of the cardio area. I could see BPM, but it would be hard for him to spot us among the equipment.

"It's not really a secret," she said, "but I don't think he'd want you to know."

I leaned closer.

"I work part-time at another gym and Jack, your bicycle pants man, used to exercise with a trainer over there. And he looked a lot different then."

"Different? How?"

"You've seen his sports car bottom?"

I nodded more vigorously than I intended. "Only clothed," I quickly added.

"At that time, which wasn't too long ago, it resembled a loaded dump truck."

I looked surprised as Irene solemnly nodded.

"It's true. He was overweight and out of shape. He was a recliner pilot, out of control with his eating and sitting. Finally at a rare doctor visit, he was told his blood pressure was through the roof and his cholesterol and triglycerides were at levels beyond measuring. He didn't smoke, but his sedentary habits were killing him. So he joined a gym and hired a trainer to help him clean up. He must have been really scared because it worked, and in less time than even I thought."

Why that big fake! He'd made derogatory comments about my appearance and my life when he'd been more out of control than I ever was! Understanding compassion should be on the top of his to-do list.

"The results seem to have been worth it," I said with a strained smile. I could now see BPM assisting a buff brunette.

"That's true. The rest of his secret is that if he doesn't stick to his exercise program, he'll slip back into the high number range. So he has to exercise. Plus the female attention he gets acts as a motivator. But when I've talked to his former trainer, he said that underneath Jack's he-man front is a kind person now concerned about living a healthy life as much as anyone else."

Well, he needed to work on loving-kindness too.

"I'll try to remember," I said.

"Please do. Because it's one of the secrets of the gym."

"Secrets of the gym?"

"Yes. There's a deeper meaning to the gym for a lot of people, way beyond what you see. Many people need to rebuild their lives. They're not here to fluff up. Time has shown them that they have to pay close attention to their bodies. True, some are here for athletic benefits, but many are ailing in some secret way and they're here because they have to be here, for prevention or for cure. There's an internal flaw they have to deal with, something they want to correct or prevent worsening.

"So when you look at people working out, don't be intimidated. Everyone has something not visible when you see their skin. You need to know their story and not just what catches your eye. Look beyond what you think you see and *don't compare your insides with their outsides.*"

"That's good advice."

"Yes, and it goes for you too, young lady. You thought all you wanted was to shape up to become more attractive. But now you've discovered there are more layers to life in the gym than just exercising.

"You've had to look at your intentions and change the patterns in your mind. You're rebuilding your body and making better choices. And you're a lot happier overall. I've even seen you smiling after a hard workout. You're on the verge of being a whole new gal, right?"

"Yes. That's absolutely true," I said.

"Well, see you later," Irene ended, with a pat on my shoulder. "Here comes your friend."

This was serious. Andrea was only a few minutes late. Her hair and face were perfect. She might have been going to an elegant restaurant, had she been dressed differently.

"Hi," she said. Behind her makeup Andrea's eyes looked tired.

"Are you all right?"

"I guess so." Then she started right in. "You remember Larry? The guy I met here?"

"Yes. I thought he was gone."

"Well, he dumped *me*!"

I knew a story was imminent and I wanted to hear and help, but before she could start, I spoke, "Andrea, I want to know what happened, but let's get going on our cardio. We can talk while we walk."

"That's fine if you'll listen and not go off to dreamland."

"Go ahead," I said as I started my treadmill. I checked my walking speed before I encouraged her to begin.

"I knew he was the one."

"I thought he was gone," I repeated.

"He was. And then I took him back," she said, her eyes misty.

"I was lonely one evening and so I played some music. When I looked at the cute notes he'd written on the CD's, I called, he came over, and we made up. He was so sweet. But after I took him back, it didn't take me long to find out the truth. He wasn't really interested in my heart or my mind. I know I'm not the kindest or the smartest person, but I do have feelings. I can't help it if my best assets are my assets, but you'd think at least one man would look at the real me. Sometimes I think I should wear baggy clothes like you do."

"I don't have them on today."

"I can see *that*! They must all be in the wash. And where'd that outfit come from anyway? Some discount store?" She glared at my new form-fitting blue and white shorts and top, and gestured. I wasn't showing sufficient sympathy.

"They're not and they did," I murmured. She went on without noticing.

"It can be hard always having to prove you have a mind when it's impossible to be heard over the roar of your appearance. Men only gawk and grab, and I'm sick of it." She stamped her foot. The treadmill rocked. "That's it! I'm going solo for a while."

"Then enjoy being happy today," I said. "These moments are precious and limited. You'll meet someone fast. Just say, 'Next!' And he'll appear, hungry-eyed and firm of tail."

"Well, aren't *you* the perky one! I thought you'd understand. I see you didn't wash your hair today. It must be full of Jon's scent and it'll smell stronger as it gets sweaty, so don't swoon. I'd be embarrassed and you'd have to lie there until a *trainer* gave you mouth-to-mouth resuscitation."

Because I was in a good mood, she'd decided to attack. Maybe she hurt more than she said; maybe she had been in love. I wasn't going to ask.

"Andrea, I do understand—so many men, and so little time; so much excitement, and so few hours; so much to buy, and so little money. I've tried to live that way too, but I've discovered I want to be with people who aren't so hurried by their lives that they overlook the qualities necessary for a prosperous relationship. And I've learned the two most important of those are loving-kindness and compassion. If you'd like, we can go for coffee and I'll explain them to you. But I want you to be calm so what I say sinks in."

"You can explain all you want, Diana," she replied, huffy. "For your information the two most important things are build and bucks. The rest is icing. If you understood men and relationships you'd see I'm right."

"I don't have your experience, Andrea, but I'll stick to compassion and loving-kindness. I need to feel I'm cared for. And I need a man to treat the minutes we share together as a treasure. I didn't understand this before, so I let the shallow scenes of television and movies set the pattern for what I thought were normal relationships."

She looked thoughtful for a few moments and then said, "Maybe you're right. And I didn't mean what I just said. I used to let my boyfriends pay my bills, but I don't anymore."

"You let your boyfriends pay your bills?" I'd never heard her confess this before and for the briefest moment I thought maybe I did have it all wrong.

"Only the ones they volunteered to pay. Because when I was happy, they were happy. I thought it was win-win, as you've always said. But I found out I was wrong. I lost and they lost. So I manage my own business now."

"Good. Then let me teach you about loving-kindness and compassion one day and you'll feel even better."

"Maybe I will," she said, "but not today. I'm upset."

"So what happened to Larry? Jim said he was studying to be a personal trainer."

"He wanted to be one, but he was too tired to be here on time in the mornings and he got yelled at for being late. Do you know people get in here at 6 a.m. and want to workout?" This seemed incredible to her.

"Why was he so tired? You overworked him at night?"

She ignored my sarcasm. "No, he was beat before he got to my place. It's a hard job being a dancer." She looked concerned.

"He was a professional dancer?" I had an image of him with a ballet troupe performing on stage before a polite, formally dressed audience.

"I don't know if you'd call it professional, although I would have never told him so. He dances at BigUns."

With this new information, my mental vision dissolved and reformed. I'd been to BigUns exactly once in my life. And I'd never forgotten.

That night a work acquaintance had a bachelorette party. I was probably invited because she didn't have enough close friends to make a quorum. The party was at BigUns and because I'd been curious, this was a good excuse to check it out. I'd have a reason to be there—to support my friend.

Located at the end of Beachway Plaza, a strip center, the place was packed with women. I'd never seen so many ladies without their men in one place at one time. It was as boisterous and rowdy as any sailor's bar I'd seen on television and just as uncouth. Greased by a few drinks, inhibitions were drained and frenzy ruled.

The place was deeper than it was wide. We had a special wedding table at the end of the stage which stuck out obscenely from the rear wall. Once seated I felt safe, temporarily, and I surveyed my surroundings. Women sat around the stage and at tables. Lit by colored lights and flashing strobes, the base of the smoke above me was about a foot from the ceiling. It would descend as the evening progressed. Stuffed full of women of all sizes and in all states of dress, the club was hot and SRO, standing room only.

As I nervously sat at the small table, my one drink minimum was delivered. The service was fast, but the drinks were tasteless iced down water with booze flavoring. As I sipped mine, Sandy, the bride-to-be, sheepishly pulled a pint of vodka from her purse. I heard other clinks. She was obviously a pro. We surreptitiously passed the pint around under the table and sweetened our drinks. My new vodka and scotch combo was a real hit.

Because she was the designated driver, one girl was sentenced to orange juice. How she was going to stand this place un-anaesthe-tized for the whole evening was beyond me. She wore the invisible badge of friendship. I envied her loyalty, but thought tonight would test its limits. I wasn't wrong.

"When's the show start?" the curly-haired brunette across the table asked to no one in particular. She had the start of a slur. Her long, crimson-tipped fingers held a micro-thin cigarette and she jabbed it at the closed curtains to add drama to her demand.

"Any minute now," our hostess replied.

"I hope Big Al, the fire dude, is here tonight." This utterance came from the smooth-haired brunette sitting to my right. She looked conservative, but her mouth hung open.

"Don't worry, Suzette. He's always here on Fridays," our hostess answered. She patted Suzette and I wondered how she knew that.

Without speaking, the blonde on my left rapped her knuckles on the table over and over, her anticipation building. The other three of us sat quietly and tried to be invisible. For me, I hoped the other women would look around me, not really see me. I admit I wanted to watch, but I didn't want to be watched while I was watching. In other words, I wanted to see the show, but I didn't want to be seen seeing and maybe enjoying the male dancers. This made sense to me.

Tension rose, the air thickened, and then accompanied by an audible whoosh from the audience, the house lights dimmed dramatically and spotlights targeted the curtains at the far end of the stage. You could see rustling movements behind them and I found myself holding my breath, *my* mouth hanging open. This was one primal scene! And with that I gained insight into my boss. The loud music now briefly increased in volume and then went silent. No one breathed.

After a few seconds of silence a dulcet female voice said, "Welcome Ladies to BigUns! We have a show planned for you this evening that will take your breath away and…leave you…panting…for…more." Airy pause with cheers and clapping. "We ask you to please remember our rules. There is no touching." Pause with boos. "If you wish to reward the dancers for their…performance…don't pull off their outfits. And finally…please remember to put out your cigarettes before approaching the stage. Their skin is…sensitive." Pause with loud awww's and clapping. "And now for your viewing pleasure BigUns is proud to present our first dancer of the evening, the ever popular Otto! Mr. Flexible!"

Wild cheers accompanied the rising music, the curtains twitched violently and a head with razor-cut hair capping a big grin poked out. Clapping and chants of "Otto, OtTO, OTTO" erupted from the unrestrained audience. The music settled into a pounding dance rhythm. Maybe this would be a lot of fun after all.

Barefoot and wearing a tuxedo tee shirt and tight black shorts, Otto jumped from behind the curtains and pounded down the stage in time with the music. He was quite a rugged guy. Women grabbed from both sides, but he was used to it and deftly avoided them. He moved smoothly for a man of his large size and as his first song ended Otto returned to his lair behind the dark curtains.

The music paused for a few moments allowing us to breathe before it returned. When it did, Otto again stuck his head out and then slowly parted the curtains. Clad only in a thong, which left little to my imagination, Otto danced his way out on the long stage. Hundreds of eyes lasered in on his assets. I was surprised his thong didn't burn off from their intensity. I lowered my gaze, not wanting to be seen staring. I was sure my face was flushed. Otto's subtitle, Mr. Flexible, was derived from the talented way he utilized back bends and handstands in his routine. The women seemed appropriately appreciative of his scantily clad gymnastics.

As I sat at our table and watched some of the women interact with the dancers, a truth came to me. Men think they hold all the cards when it comes to bravery. But I know women have it in equal measure to men. With both men and women, courage and fear are two sides of the same coin. You cannot have one without the other. It's only a matter of which side is face up.

Some women were bold. They walked right up to a dancer and put their dollars into his thong. Others were timid and either didn't have the courage to poke in their appreciation or got a more adventurous pal to do it for them. Some would tilt their head and let the dancer kiss them on the cheek as a thank you. But one woman was more scheming. When a dancer bent to kiss her upturned cheek, she quickly twisted her head, grabbed the back of his head with her hand and pulled his lips down onto hers. When the shocked stripper jerked back, I saw her tongue withdraw from his mouth. She licked her lips. The crowd clapped, cheered, and patted her on the back and arms as she triumphantly returned to her seat.

I had the fearful side of the coin face up that evening, at first, and joined in with my group as best I could. They hooted and hollered; they waved and shook their fists; they made lewd and suggestive comments; they yelled at the other women to shut the hell up. Sandy didn't look ready for marriage, but Suzette was pleased with Big Al's performance and tipped him ten dollars. I kept my cool reserve until a strange thing happened.

The lights dimmed and then rose as the last dancer of the show came on stage. His name was Joaquin and he was keen to say the very least. Earlier, I'd seen some of the other performers focus on one or two women in the audience while they danced. Sometimes these women enjoyed the attention; sometimes they tried to hide under their tables. I was glad I'd been ignored. That was until Joaquin appeared. He was not overly tall or overly muscular, but he was sleek and oh, so fine.

And when he returned for his second scene, minus his red and black bullfighter's outfit and the rose in his mouth, our eyes met and locked. I was the subject of his strut. I couldn't run; I couldn't hide; I couldn't even look away. I was frozen to my seat. He stared at me as he danced. My eyes drank him down, and I understood the word mesmerize. We hadn't met or even touched, but I was hooked. And maybe he's hooked on me, too, I fantasized; maybe I'm the one that's desirable.

"Here," Sandy said. She stuffed a five dollar bill into my numb right hand.

"No. I can't do it. I can't go up there." My voice was husky.

"Yes, you can." This from the blonde was grinning at my predicament. She knew my rear was filled with the lead of fear.

"I can't..."

"Well, I will," Suzette said, and snatched Sandy's money.

"No you don't! He's mine!" I said louder than I'd intended and pulled the bill from her fingers. I could not believe I'd said that.

Then, panting, I staggered to my feet, but as I stood still with many expectant eyes burning me, I panicked. My nerve failed and I sat down and down and down, all the way to the floor. I hadn't seen Suzette pull my chair back. That concrete was damn hard!

Laughter roared. "She's got it bad!" was the mildest comment my dazed brain understood over the booming music.

Amidst clapping, I returned to my feet. Now the coin had flipped over and courage was on top. I stood up straight, pulled back my shoulders, and then went forward, my heart pounding. I'd been shaken but not stirred from my purpose and was ready to give everything to a guy I didn't know.

When I finally reached an empty spot at the side of the stage a kind of hush fell, at least for me. I'd done it. I was within range of his touch.

Joaquin stared into my eyes with interested amusement and then danced closer, farther, closer. It was a teasing parody of the mating ritual. He wanted to arouse in me as much interest as he could. And it worked. I wasn't leaving. I wanted my kiss, plus a lot more.

Powered by my new bravery and the scotch and vodka combos, I folded the five length-wise and put it between my teeth so the end stuck out. Joaquin exposed a diamond white smile as he danced nearer and nearer. I trembled with fear, boldness, and excitement.

When he came close enough for me to smell his sweat, I tilted my head back. And as he bent to grab the five with his teeth, I heard him whisper so only I could hear, "Mi amor." When I felt his tug, I opened my mouth and released the bill.

At that same moment a woman to my left reached up and stroked Joaquin's shiny thigh, and above. She surprised him and as he quick-stepped back he slipped on a slick spot of his own male sweat and with a groaning "uhhhh," he toppled backwards and bounced on his firm, thonged bottom.

Then as loud snaps and pops startled me, the end of the stage collapsed and sent Joaquin sliding on his rump like a human bowling ball with money in its mouth down its ramp and—Wham!—into our table. It was a strike! Drinks and women went everywhere.

At the same time there was crashing and smashing as women jumped to avoid the falling stage and the flailing Joaquin. And the damage rippled outward as those women overturned the tightly packed tables behind them.

Only seconds had passed, but the noise seemed to go on forever. A totem of male heads, topped by Otto, peered from between the curtains as the music pounded its beat and strobe lights bounced off broken glass and reflected in the expanding drink pools.

The music suddenly cut off and the house lights flashed on to reveal a sea of wreckage. Things like this only happened in the movies or to Andrea.

My friends, sprawled on the floor with their party clothes soaking up liquor, glared up at me as Joaquin staggered past. He was robotic, the spell broken, the five gone. He didn't even look my way.

The dulcet voice returned, "We've had a little…accident. The next show will be…delayed." Pause with silence. "Make yourselves comfortable and we'll be back to our entertainment…shortly." The voice cut off and the music came back on.

Head lowered, I joined the women crunching en masse for the quiet safety outside as I heard ugliness directed at me. "What'd she do to him?" "Is she drunk or what?" And from my own group: "You can't take Diana anywhere!" "It's always the quiet ones!"

I wanted to yell, "It wasn't my fault!" But my bravery had fled. So I kept my head down and stamped out. I was a convenient patsy toward whom they could vent their frustration. After I'd suffered sufficiently, I thought, "Too bad! Their husbands or boyfriends won't let them come back." I caught my own cab home and later dreamed of the sleek Joaquin.

"See, Diana, I knew you'd fade out on me."

"Sorry. I was thinking about your ex-boyfriend working at Big-Uns," I said, my mind back at Four Palms. "It's quite a place."

"When were *you* there?" she asked with wonder.

"I went with some girls from work."

Andrea looked relieved. "Well, I'd be scared to go in there because Larry told me the women get violent. Once, a woman got so worked up, she grabbed one of the dancers, threw him to the stage, and caused a big mess."

I blushed, but didn't think she noticed.

"What could get into a poor woman like that?" she continued. "Frustrated sex drive I guess. No, I'll wait and see Larry at home. Or at least I used to." This brought a tear to her eye, but I'm sure it was for Larry and not for the poor, frustrated, and violent woman.

"Well, I've had enough walking and Four Palms for one day," Andrea said with a last few teary sniffs. "But I have an idea. The art festival is at the park next weekend. Let's go and hunt for treasures. You can pick me up on Saturday at eleven. My car won't have gas, so we'll take yours."

I nodded okay. But wondered how she knew her car would be out of gasoline in a week.

"Good. See you. Call me if something or someone comes up." She bounced off her treadmill and I let her go.

I was thinking. Tonight…well…tonight was Good Ol' Saturday Night.

Maybe, just maybe, I'd go back to BigUns. Alone.

Mi amor was waiting there for me.

# Chapter Nineteen:
## Threads of Life and Love

*"You can't change someone else, but you have
control over your own thoughts."*

We circled and dodged near the art festival and finally located a parking space. It was farther away than I wanted, but closer than I'd expected. Then as we pounded along the endless sidewalk it dawned on me that the sun was in the wrong place in the sky.

"About face! Forward march!" I told Andrea, and then ignored her unpleasant commentary. At least I'd figured out the problem. Left to her, we could have ended up anywhere. So now as she hastily ate her breakfast nachos, that resembled the woodchips beneath our feet, all was right with her world.

Then up ahead I saw a familiar profile. As it came nearer my heart leapt—and then smashed down hard into the dirt. It was Jon and...he was with someone *else*! He was with the *woman* from Four Palms!

I stopped, and then it started. Uncontrollable surges of white-hot lava burned in my veins and mind and quickly became my emotional sap as every feeling known to woman cried out in torment. I thought we were doing so well together! I guess I was wrong! Loathsome thoughts flowed into and out of my brain, steam poured from my ears, and I sent fire shooting from my eyes. I was sure my hat was melting.

"You look hot. Do you need something to drink?" Andrea asked, and turned to see what my attention was focused on. "What is it? Those men don't look interesting."

"I thought I saw Jon, but it couldn't have been him. You're right. I am thirsty."

We got two vanilla root beers and I collapsed onto the needles under a pine tree. Their prickles brought me down to earth and I wished I'd brought along a little bottle of scotch.

"Was it really Jon? Why didn't you go talk to him?"

"He was with someone else, a woman from the gym!"

"A *gym* woman!"

"Yes, a client." But she must be much more than just a client, my weary heart said.

"Where are they? Let *me* talk to them! If anyone knows how to run off another woman, it's me!"

"No, Andrea, just let them be. If Jon wants to be with someone else, then let him. I don't know what I have to offer anyway. She's got a pretty face, a great looking body. I can't compete."

"There's no competition. There's only you. And you can have him if you want. She's a floozy, as your grandmother would have said. But you have real depth to you and that's what men want. That's what matters." She sounded shocked to be saying this.

"Yes, but Jon wants someone who makes skillful choices and my life has been so messed up."

"No. He wants *you*. Why do you think he spends the extra effort to work with you? To get your life in order so you two can have a real relationship. Besides, you've told me how balanced he is, how he's looking for loving-kindness and compassion. You've got them. Or at least you're getting them. And pretty soon your outsides will match your insides and then you'll be HWP! And that's that." She slapped her hands together.

As I listened, I perked up. "Oh, Andrea. Sometimes I don't know what I'd do without a friend like you. Even if a lot of what you say are only guesses, at least your guesses make me feel good."

"They are *not* guesses, Diana," she replied with a snort. "They're based on my woman's intuition, which is highly tuned, as you well know."

I wondered how it was so highly tuned for me and not for her, but her attempt to make me feel better had worked. "Thanks for being here."

"You're welcome. Now come on. Those people are buying things we've got to have."

We browsed, but my heart wasn't in it and I didn't last, so we sat down again on the needles.

"He must be special," Andrea said.

"Oh, he's special all right. Jon's the most special person I've ever known."

"So, is he *more* than a friend?"

"No, just a friend...only a friend."

"No bare-belly rubbing?"

"No...not at all. We've had coffee, dinner, gone to the beach, the park, and to the faire. But nothing intimate."

"Don't you at least talk about sex, or money?"

"We don't talk about either. It's not that kind of relationship."

"Then what do you do? Have boring political discussions? If there's no sex or money, it must be dry, like salad with no dressing, or coffee without amaretto."

"It's not boring at all. We talk about everything: life, love, and the pursuit of happiness. We have a wonderful time and there's no pressure to do, say, or even be other than who we are. It's impossible for me to wear a mask, Jon sees right through it. That was scary at first, but now I feel really free."

"Well, men like that don't exist. He must want something, otherwise what's he get?"

"You're right. He does want two things."

"Aha, I knew it! What are they?" Andrea leaned close, not wanting anyone to overhear.

In keeping, I whispered, "First, Jon wants me to attain happiness. And second, he wants me to teach others how to do the same."

Her face was a palette of shifting emotional colors: surprise, disbelief, irritation, sadness, and finally acceptance. She wasn't going to get what she wanted because it didn't exist; she was not going to get some sleazy story.

"It must be true. I can't believe you'd make up something like that," she finally said.

"It is true. I'd heard of men like him, but never knew where to find one."

"So tell me, are you in love with Jon, or is he in love with you? Or more importantly, do you think this could be *permanent?*" Her words arrowed my heart.

I knew if I said no to her questions she would be unhappy for me, but if I said yes she would be unhappy for herself. The answer was neither.

"We never even got around to talking about those things," I said longingly and miserable as I thought about him with the blond.

"I understand. Maybe it's better not to hurry," she said with cheerful optimism. "He's a good catch and you don't want him to get frightened away."

I guess Andrea viewed Jon as a hooked fish, like some snapper for me to reel in at my leisure, but I was glad she'd forgotten about my side of the love issue. I could have answered that question easily.

"Let's walk," Andrea said as she shook off pine needles. "Sitting too long can make you lazy."

We shopped for artists' wares for about an hour, petted llamas and goats, and watched a red-haired woman being helped from a blue portable toilet overturned by some boys playing football. She was unhurt, but hysterical. And all the while I looked around until I determined Jon was nowhere to be seen. Maybe he left.

Finally, we made our way to the food pavilion. It was a giant open-air tent under tall, green pines. We ordered veggie burgers, sodas, and a big pile of salty fries. We promised each other not to tell anyone about the fries.

"I thought you were here," came a voice above my left ear. "May we join you?"

Fries went flying as Jon sat beside me and the *blond* woman sat next to Andrea, whose eyes bulged as half-chewed veggie burger pieces dribbled down her chin.

The rush of feelings I'd calmed resumed their roar. Barely able to control myself, I sat motionless. I was not going to get angry or cry or both. And as those feelings arose I tried to let them go. But after less than a minute I felt a violent shriek brewing in my chest. I wasn't going to be able to stop this one and as its pressure peaked, I saw Andrea glance at me.

"I don't believe it!" Andrea grinned, and wiped her mouth with her dirty napkin. "We just talked about you and *here* you are. She's told me how wonderful you are and how she adores you. And not just for your assets." She gestured.

"Is that true?" he asked. Behind his dark glasses I imagined Jon's eyes had their amused glow. He hadn't acknowledged my raging battle and he wasn't embarrassed by Andrea's wit.

But the unhappy, bubbling shriek still wanted out.

"And what assets are those?" Jon looked at me, eyes now barely visible.

But before my mind had cooled enough to engage my mouth, Andrea spoke again. "You know what assets—your strength, your balance, your smarts. She's told me how much you've helped her and that she'll repay you whenever and however you want." She folded her arms under her breasts.

"Is that true?" Must have been his phrase of the day.

I quickly stuffed the squirming shriek into a mental bag before I answered, "Oh, Andrea always exaggerates, and it's been a long time since we talked about you. You only came up briefly because I saw you looking at pottery with...?" I aimed friendly, but my teeth and fillings ground.

"Please excuse me," he said. "This is Corinne. She's a friend from the gym."

So she's a *friend* from the gym. Then what's she doing *here*? This isn't the gym and she should stay *there*! She's not allowed out here! But then...is that how he sees me too...as a friend from the gym? Weary from its anguish, my poor heart decided not to pursue. I sighed. But because there was no guilty hesitancy in his introduction, I collected myself and told Corinne my name. Then after Andrea introduced herself we waited for someone to speak.

After a sip, he patted my arm and said, "I told Corinne we workout together and she wanted to meet you. She has something to share. Maybe you can get together, perhaps over coffee."

"That'll be fine," I said tightly. "Whenever you want. Let me know."

"How about now, Diana?" Corinne replied.

Surprised, I looked at Andrea who nodded her approval. She was more interested in checking out my teacher than in a tale from Corinne, but she'd listen, especially if it justified something she'd done.

Corinne had a generous mouth and when she smiled, blended in her liquid eyes, and added a pinch of her slinky figure, any man would be dead meat, a term used by my former friend Tracy when prowling. No wonder Jon was enraptured. Even I felt her power.

"Jon," Corinne began, "believes telling you about my life might illustrate some of the things you've been discussing.

"When I was younger, I was very unappreciative. I smiled and whatever I wanted came to me. My pleasures—monetary, sexual, or whatever—were requirements for everyone, and I had no regrets. If someone didn't please me, out they went. And this was true for anyone: parents, siblings, employers, friends, lovers. Later, a glance and tight clothes got me what I wanted. My life revolved around using everyone.

"Then I fell in love with a man who was, of course, inappropriate. I'd cry about his antics to anyone who'd listen, and that was a very small crowd, most of whom were glad to see me get my due. Once though, while complaining about his latest infidelity, one woman asked me, 'In the past, how did you treat men?'

"For the first time I answered honestly and admitted that sometimes I treated them like roaches. I didn't care about their feelings because there was always an endless supply."

"Then she asked, 'So how are you being treated now?'"

"I realized I was receiving what I'd dished out. I'd created suffering for others and now I was being treated in the same callous manner. But what I didn't understand until I met your teacher was the time factor. I thought if there were no immediate repercussions, then there were no consequences. Now I've learned the truth.

"Jon taught me there are four parts to a hurtful action. First, there is having someone or something to hurt. Second, there is the intention or want to cause suffering. Third, there is the causing of suffering through word or deed. And finally, there is the satisfaction of having done the hurtful thing. The second and fourth parts may be brief, but they're always present any time you cause suffering for another."

Corrine continued, "When you perform an unskillful action it sets up a long thread that plays out behind you in time rather than in space and this cord connects you to the past hurtful deed until something comes along and pulls it, creating an action that inflicts retribution on you. And since your earlier unskillful choice may be years in the past and forgotten, whatever happens to balance it always comes as a surprise. Plus its magnitude is greater because time has woven the thread into a rope."

"Give me an example," Andrea said as she chewed limp fries.

"All right," Corinne said. "Suppose someone plans to steal, steals, and then feels good about stealing five dollars from a friend who trusts them. This action sets up a thread in time. Years later when the earlier theft has long been forgotten and usually when the former thief can least afford it, something unexpected happens and it costs him over five hundred dollars. The thread is pulled. His life is now balanced as to the past hurtful action. The same thing happens in relationships, as I found out. And now that I've learned this truth," she concluded, "I avoid actions or words that cause anguish."

I could see Andrea becoming upset, so I asked, "Say you've done some things you feel remorse about. Is there anything you can do to reduce the pain when the strings are tugged?"

"Yes, there is," Jon said. "You can't change your unskillful acts. They will come back to see you in some way or another. But you can mitigate their potency by choosing new actions based on kindness, generosity, and compassion. These help balance the earlier pain you caused. And that way you don't create another thread to be yanked in your future."

"Do you mean if someone hurts me, I shouldn't get even?" Andrea asked. She wasn't used to a deep discussion in a food tent on a warm sunny day while eating cold fries dripping with sour ketchup. But she'd wanted to know more about my teacher and now she was having her questions answered, up close and personal.

"No," Jon said. In 'getting even' you believe you act from a place of 'rightness,' but you're not. What the other person did wasn't skillful, but if you create any additional suffering through unskillful actions of your own, then more suffering will be inflicted back on you in the future. It's the old eye for an eye mentality. It has never worked and it never will."

"But if bad things continue to happen to me, do I *still* sit around and do nothing?" Andrea placed her burger in the sunlight that slanted across the end of the table.

"Do nothing unskillful, nothing unkind. Anything beyond this creates more threads. Don't react from a place of anger or fear. Do what's necessary, but do it from a place of calm resolve."

Andrea rubbed her temples and I knew how she felt. As it expanded with new information, your head ached.

"Corinne, here's your sister," my teacher said, and rose.

Corinne's sister and a girlfriend joined us. As we introduced ourselves the sinking feeling returned. Damn, more competition.

The four of them visited and then Corinne's sister said, "I'm sorry, but we need to go. Corinne has a busy week ahead."

"What she means," Corinne said, "is I have more chemotherapy and that it wears me out."

Andrea gasped as Corinne continued, "Jon works with me at Four Palms between chemo rounds to build my strength because the treatments leave me so weak, I couldn't do anything that would tear me down further. So Jon, my doctor, and I set up my program together, one that makes me feel strong, and here I am today out in the fresh air and having a wonderful time. Life has taken on renewed meaning."

Neither Andrea nor I had anything to say. A buzzing horsefly flew into her open mouth and she spat it out without comment.

Standing, Corinne said, "You didn't think this was my real hair? If you did, then this was worth every cent." And she reached up and pulled off her blond wig. She was completely bald!

There were no words to say. There was nothing to say at all. My thoughts and judgments drained away like sewage.

"You didn't know, did you?" She laughed. "I'd never been a blonde, but when this unexpected opportunity presented itself I decided to make the most of it." She replaced her hair.

"I want to make one point clear however," she said, more seriously, and bent towards us. "I don't feel my disease is related to the subject we discussed. However, I do think my lifestyle may have had a hand in it. And as for me, I'm at that age when things sometimes start to go awry. All the more reason to remember how great life is."

"It was nice meeting you all, but we must be going," Corinne's sister repeated. "It's a long walk to the car and I want us to go before the crowds leave."

Corinne gave Jon a peck on the cheek and then waved as the three of them vanished into the crowd.

After they left, we sat and enjoyed the afternoon breeze. Maybe it was my imagination, but I was certain when Jon looked at me it was different from the way he looked at Corinne. That seemed clear to me now, but when I was burning in anger, not recalling how it comes from fear, I'd been unable to see or feel anything else. When I looked back, I was so glad I hadn't said or done anything spiteful. While I was attached to my thoughts I could have driven away exactly what I sought. Tears watered my eyes when I imagined those inner tormentors getting their way. I would have gained nothing but sorrow, a sorrow experienced equally by both the giver and the receiver.

This was very different from my usual manner when I believed that my self-righteous anger yielded happy results. I'd get what I thought I wanted, but almost immediately it'd slip away. Now, I saw that the experience of anger itself was the true madness because it doesn't fix or heal the fear and I could choose not to go there. I knew that Fear plus Anger, in thought, word, or deed, equaled Misery and Enmity, in all of life.

Andrea shook and stretched herself into the present. She got another soda, more fries, and then picked up her sun-warmed burger and finished eating it.

"Okay, Jon, Mr. Trainer-Teacher, I've got a question for you," she said as she licked her lips. "What about people who'll hurt you for no reason at all, even kill you? Kindness won't fix them."

"A difficult question," he said, "and with many things to consider, but I'll give you my interpretation.

"The kind of person you're talking about creates suffering as a crutch. They feel confusion, resentment, and frustration, in a word, powerlessness. And the target of their hate is what they want the most, inner strength, balance, and the knowledge of how they fit into the world, in another word, happiness. But their thoughts convince them they must create misery to relieve their own dissatisfactions, however they only bolster their own anguish, they get no relief.

"Their actions can range from the ordinary, such as Jack getting his truck scratched, to murder, the ultimate 'You're not OK.' When in reality it is the person who committed the act who is not 'OK.'

"It's a pyramid of pain. The base is broad and composed of many small vicious acts and as you progress upward the number of acts becomes less, but the severity increases. When you reach the top the act is horrendous and could affect many people. Examples would be a base of burglary to a peak of senseless murder. Or on a larger scale, a base of murder to a peak of war.

"Sadly, the brief moments of pleasurable gloating the perpetrators experience afterwards become addictive, and so they continue their agony-causing ways."

"In other words," Andrea said, "they are not having a happy time and they want you to join them, or they want to force you to join them."

"Brief, but that's it."

"But how do you make them stop?"

"There isn't a simple solution," my teacher answered. "Some advocate continuing to turn the other cheek. Others say that when fear and anger reach a fever pitch, then that person should be treated like a rabid dog because the misery they suffer inside is so overwhelming, they have become deranged. And so you'd avoid a rabid dog, not go into his yard, but if he attacked, you'd be justified in protecting yourself. Which is correct? I cannot answer for you. The answer has to come from within your own heart."

Andrea had a concerned look.

"Okay. Just one, no two, more." She leaned forward. "What do you tell someone who has been a victim? Or more importantly, what do you tell yourself?"

Jon thought for a minute.

"My response to your questions has three parts," he said, using his fingers to count.

"First, the victims always want to know, 'Why?' My answer to them is: ignorance by the perpetrator who, unaware of their own inner torment and knowing so little about how to obtain the happiness they so desperately want, lashes out because they know no other way. Reminding yourself of this helps to keep it in perspective.

"Second, it's difficult for the mind to grasp something when it falls far beyond normal life. During this disbelief the victims suffer. Be kind to them, and to yourself. Help both return to balance and take comfort in spiritual beliefs, whatever they may be. Your spiritual center is a beacon of inner strength in times of trouble.

"Lastly, let them say what they need to say and you feel what you need to feel, but avoid striking back. You must choose your battles wisely and never act in haste. If you don't, you become your own persecutor and the perpetrator has achieved his plan. But the most important thing to know is that you have a choice. You can't change someone else, but you have control over your own thoughts.

"And remember, the number of kind people always outweighs the number causing the distress, so we must place a strong emphasis on unity. We all desire the same things and we all suffer in the same ways. All must help the one and the one must join in and help the all."

Our discussion had touched somewhere deep within each of us so when Andrea began to ask again, I shushed her. We'd had enough for today. Jon excused himself to get us fresh drinks.

"Well, you certainly have an interesting friend," Andrea said as she watched him stride. "You *are* a lucky girl!"

# Chapter Twenty: A Slap and a Dash

*"And when the anger was gone I saw I could come
from a place of calm—and still get what I wanted."*

It was Monday night again and after what had happened earlier that day I was surprised to be at the gym; I was surprised to be sane.

At first I tried a fast walk on the treadmill to outpace my racing thoughts, but it didn't work. They crowded me, made me stumble. Then when one pitched me into the control panel, I decided I needed a safer way to calm myself.

I had been early and Jon was late. A client had gone overtime and now Jim wanted to keep me company. But his time could have been better spent elsewhere. He caught up with me on my way to the "X" room.

"I've been working days so I haven't seen you for a while. How's everything?"

"Just fine," I said and didn't stop. This didn't discourage him.

"You're shaping up! I'm glad you've stuck with your program."

"I am too." But my faster metabolism couldn't keep up with my mind.

"You know I took your advice," he said, and kept in step.

"What advice?" No one was interested in what I might have to say.

"To keep a journal. Thank you."

"You're welcome," I muttered.

"May I take you to dinner Friday night for helping me?"

"No, I have a workout on Friday."

"I meant afterwards. I've cleared it with Jon."

Already in a bad mood, his comment pushed me to the edge.

"You don't have to clear *anything* with him," I said, and made one of Andrea's gestures. "If you'd asked *me* first, it might have been a date. Now, forget it." I hadn't broken my stride.

"Well...ah...sorry. I'll remember that. So that means no?"

I nodded and entered the exercise room. The truth could just be damned.

My muscles were leather hard and all my stretching accomplished was to release more toxic memories.

That morning a meeting had been called to review the budget. The division's spending was in line with projections, but Mr. Dawl wanted a big reduction because he feared for the size of his bonus. Everyone knew that last unspoken fact because a yacht salesman was the boss's new best friend. So the secret formula for the meeting was less spent equaled more efficiency equaled bigger bonus equaled fancy new boat equaled family harmony.

His anger, powered by fear, poured out onto all of us. If he hadn't been serious, his performance would have been comical.

"We'll have to ditch all the temporaries and others too," he bellowed, chins flapping. "They're too damn many bodies sitting around here sipping and gabbing when we need work done. We have to get more done with less. Hey! That's it! More with less! I like it! That's our new motto. Now don't forget it! Very pleased with himself, he sat down and his flushed face beamed with pride.

I knew one reason for firing the contract workers was because of Tina. He'd targeted her for his next colored paper rendezvous, but she'd refused and he was mad about being snubbed. We waited while Mr. Dawl recharged. We knew he had more than one blast in him. Luckily, it was brief.

"Now get to your offices and report back here at two! Sharp! And your recommendations for cuts had better be big. Remember our new slogan—more with less!" People jumped, papers rustled, and everyone hustled. It was a vending machine lunch for us again.

Later, during the noon hour, I chewed a cardboard and mustard flavored sandwich as I planned my comments. I wasn't a manager, but recently I'd been included in some of those meetings. The supervisory position in my department was open and I wanted to believe it was my penchant for details and being considered for a promotion that had gotten me invited, although sometimes an inner voice said that it was only to keep his memory of me fresh. But as I swallowed the stringy bites, I decided to tell the truth as I saw it.

I remembered Edward, who'd been fired after picking kindness over rightness, but I wouldn't be doing that...exactly. I would only be watching out for the company. The survivors couldn't handle the increased workload, so everyone would be affected, Mr. Dawl included. What I'd be doing by being truthful would be saving everyone a lot of unnecessary suffering. Better to speak up now than to deal with the consequences later.

The heart knows right from wrong so this was the natural thing for me. I thought I might have a problem, but once I'd made my decision I found that the needed courage was there. Being outspoken would be new for me so I spent the last of the lunch hour organizing my thoughts and jotting down notes and figures. By meeting time, I was ready.

✦

Reassembled at two, we waited. About twenty minutes later, Mr. Dawl tramped in. His caster-footed chair attempted to escape his bulk, but he corralled it.

"Let's hear it," he barked. And we were off. After an hour, it was my turn.

Before, I'd always been nervous when speaking to a group. I'd even broken out in red splotches on my face and neck. But now as he pointed his fat finger at me, I took a deep breath…and I let go of past meetings and my blotchy embarrassment, I let go of the future and criticisms, and I let go of dramas about myself and others running through my Mundane Mind. And focused in my Open Sky Mind I centered only on my presentation, in the moment as it unfolded.

"Now is not the time to reduce my department's portion of the budget," I began as I passed out copies of the figures I'd amassed during lunch and explained them.

My words punched his gut. He snapped back and then squirmed in his chair.

I continued, "With the new partnership we've just established, if we cut into the areas outlined, we won't be able to follow through. The papers are signed, the commitment made. Projections indicate an increase in staffing needed for this quarter alone. Not to mention the entire overhead associated with this new joint venture. I'm also concerned our division and its management will be in trouble with the home office." As I spoke I thought my reasons made sense, but…I'd assumed wrong.

There was silence. I'd explained my points logically and unemotionally, and to me, I'd been successful. I didn't think there would be total agreement, but I did expect some open minds and perhaps a change in direction. I shouldn't have bothered.

Mr. Dawl didn't know what to say. I guess I was the only person who'd ever rendered him speechless. Finally huffing and puffing, he reared back and my hair was blown out behind me.

"That's got to be one of the most ridiculous damn things that's ever reared its ugly head, Ms. Archer," he began, warming up. "Who gives a damn about the home office? Let those asses watch their own pimply rears like I've got to watch mine. And who the hell do you think gives even a tiny damn about the staff? If they don't want to work, let them get the hell out of here! I can't be worried about their little snivels and whines! If they want a life let them get it somewhere else. It's no damn concern of mine and none of yours either."

"But to be diplomatic," Mr. Dawl continued, and raised his hands to take in everyone, "is there anyone who agrees with her? Say so now or keep your damn mouths shut!"

Silence of the grave.

"That's right!" he yelled. "No one else shares your damn perverted view. They see we have to cut, cut, cut. And it's got to be done now, now, now. I know you think you've got some hotshit ideas, but nobody gives a damn! And I know you think because you're a woman you can get your flowery underwear in an uproar and nurture every damn person, but the people here have got to work, work, work, if they want pay, pay, pay." Sputtering, he pounded on the table. Heat had melted his mindsprings. "And one last thing, Ms. Archer, you won't get any damn favors from me no matter how much you can put out." Now while this sounded like Mr. Dawl was talking about my work, it was obvious to all he meant something different.

Embarrassed down to my toes, I had nothing further to say.

Then after a final withering look the focus of his wrath moved on to his next victim.

Acquiescence returned.

But as I stretched, the day's stress leaked away. I was thankful I'd chosen to be at Four Palms rather than at home cooking and wine-ing my wounds, or out shopping.

"How are you tonight, Diana?" It was Jon. Wrapped in my tight thoughts, I hadn't noticed him approach.

"I'm fine. No that's not true, I was angry, but now I'm more disappointed." And I was nervous about my job. I couldn't recall anyone not bowing and kissing Mr. Dawl's toes or whatever, like he was a god. I believed I'd offered management vital information to help them make the correct decision for the good of all. The fact I hadn't kissed-up would eat at him like a tumor until he lost his remaining sanity. What I would face tomorrow, I didn't know. And if I thought about it too hard, I'd cry.

"It must be big," Jon said, observant as always. Then, "Because I'm running late, let's do a short arm and ab workout tonight followed by coffee. We'll make it up tomorrow evening."

Jim interrupted once trying to invite himself along. I told him no.

But later while getting my things, I decided it might be good to have another person there. Edward hadn't minded my presence and Jim looked upset since I'd seen him earlier. I told my teacher to tell Jim he could to come along for coffee as long as he'd behave himself. You know how salesmen can be.

Hands around a warm mug, I told my story succinctly. I added neither curses nor negative descriptions of Mr. Dawl, no matter how much he reminded me of barnyard animals, or feces. When I concluded the silence lasted for a few minutes.

"I would have knocked him silly," Jim said, "then out run him."

"That wouldn't have been appropriate," Jon said. "True, his behavior was intolerable, but violence solves nothing."

"What would you do?" I asked.

"That isn't simple," Jon replied. "There are questions that need to be answered before deciding. One solution might be to leave. Ask yourself, 'How much do I compromise my mental and physical well being by staying? How financially important is this job?' Remember most people assume their physical health will always be perfect. Their mental health is another subject. What you faced today was nothing more than a grown up bully armed with the knowledge you'd be afraid to fight back. That mental whipping degrades the body and makes it prone to illness. And then there is the isolation from working long hours."

"I'd still slap the crap out of him," Jim said.

"So you're faced with a choice, go or stay, with the knowledge your boss isn't going to change. But if you do leave, you must organize your departure carefully. Do not act in haste."

"I agree," I said. "Plus your description of isolation fits me perfectly."

"Right now you don't know what to do," Jon said, "but things change so remember to always have backup plans to reduce fear and keep you calm. And put them on paper. That way you can review or modify them easily."

"And lastly, remember too that the good can become the enemy of the better."

"That's a lot to think about." But I did feel less fearful.

"Go ahead Diana, make your plans," Jim said. "Then whack him upside his head."

We laughed.

That was Monday. On Friday, it wasn't funny anymore.

The intervening days were peaceful like the calm before the storm. When I saw Mr. Dawl in the hallways, he was cordial. Nothing was mentioned about the infamous meeting, much to my relief. I kept a low profile.

Then on Friday afternoon heads rolled at one o'clock when the managers spread the layoff virus. Those plague-free scurried away and hid.

"The faster it's cleaned up, the less it'll stink," was Mr. Dawl's latest motto and he'd decided I was to be the first to go. But at lunch with Andrea it'd taken forever to get the check, so I was late getting back.

I looked up from the pile on my desk as the boss's secretary came to my door.

"Where have you been? He's been searching for you." I followed her to his office.

"Shut the door," he said as I entered. "Sit down."

Mr. Dawl didn't say anything for a minute or so. He just sat staring at me. I tried not to meet his eyes.

His office was a sty. Candy bar wrappers haloed his overflowing trash can, someone had wrestled in the papers on his desk, a crunched blind dangled precariously, and a dusty deer head minus one eye hung on a wall. I smelled juniper.

"For someone who's as pretty as you are Ms. Archer, you aren't too smart. No one much at home I guess." His chair emitted a groan.

I swallowed.

"And you don't want to be a team player. All that crap about the poor staff is—crap. If they didn't like their checks they'd be gone before you could take a piss.

"Now even with our realigned priorities I'd planned on keeping you because you had uses, but you embarrassed me. So no matter what you've got, it isn't worth you causing trouble. To cut to the bottom line, here's your severance. We could have made beautiful music, but you're one sour note. That's for damn sure!"

Tears welled. Inside I was shaking with anger. Women hold in anger; men hold in tears.

"Cat got your tongue?" My silence was unnerving him. "Well, shut the door on your way out and don't let the knob hit you in the ass."

Stunned—not even a simple thank you for my years of service—I went to my office to collect my odds and ends. Heads were low. The survivors were terrified of contagion.

Humiliated, I carried what little I was keeping to my car. When I returned for an old, half-dead plant that would have a better chance with me, Mr. Dawl came in.

"Look, Diana," he said quietly, "I know you're upset, but we can fix things."

I must have looked hopeful.

"If you're flexible we can work things out, and the fact that we've been close makes it better for both of us."

I was silent and there was an air of disbelief. The hatchet wanted to hug the wood?

"I mean," he continued, "if we agree to hold regular meetings to review our feelings then you can put your things back and we'll forget this unpleasantness. We'll pretend it was an error in communication. How's that sound? Sounds good to me. And like you're so fond of saying, it's win-win."

Remembering what my teacher had said, I wanted to refuse with as little emotion as possible. I didn't want to burn bridges. But as I turned to face him, his left hand grabbed my rear and his right hand fondled my breast. An "Oh!" sighed into my ear.

I spun around and saw Tina the temp outside my office. Then my hand, powered by all the stress and abuse, slapped. The impact

was firecracker loud, set my ears to ringing and my fingers to sting-
ing. And although serious, part of my mind was laughing. His
bloated face had turned to gelatin! The skin compressed leaving
a palm and finger shaped impression that slowly filled with red.
His stubby nose shook and his chins flapped like droopy drapes
disturbed by a sudden dusty gust. An onion belch blew through
his pursed lips. Tina hurried away.

My initial reaction was disbelief. Good girls didn't do things
like that! But shock quickly turned into action and before he
could recover and maybe hit me back, I grabbed my purse and the
plant and dashed out of my office and out of the building. Then
I rocketed my car out of the parking lot, almost sideswiping a
pickup blocking the exit lane, and didn't slow down until I saw I
was headed for Clearwater instead of home.

That evening I called in sick to my teacher. Feelings were throb-
bing and I didn't trust myself outside. I was only being protective,
but felt like I'd committed a crime. And I understood how disem-
powered a person can become. To save myself, I'd done something
I thought wrong and I was feeling guilty. Now my career was in
shambles; my continuity lost.

"What did I do to make him come on to me? Why did I lose
control?"

I spent the weekend beaten senseless by an emotional pendulum
which swung from fury to self-recrimination. On occasion it struck
a hot note of fear and when it did, cold sweat sprung out. At first
the fear was about losing what I had: my apartment, my car, and
my belongings. But as the weekend passed, it changed into being
afraid I wouldn't get what I deserved: my desirability, my teacher,
and my happy new life. Sometimes I choked on sheer panic.

By Sunday evening I was unwashed and exhausted. Books and papers were scattered everywhere, the kitchen counters were stacked high with dirty dishes, and the bed sheets were sticky from sweat. But finally, quiet settled over my mind.

Then I stripped off my three-day-old clothes, ran a tub of hot water, added one of the oils from the medieval faire, and relaxed in it as a liquid image coated my mind.

I was in the chocolate bath. And as it warmed my core, fear melted away. Tomorrow didn't yet exist, but it would be a better tomorrow because I was alive and loved. Not necessarily by anyone else, but loved by *me*. I was precious to myself, and we would be happy together no matter what, my best and most loving friend and I.

The phone rang early Monday. It was Tina the temp. She'd gotten my number from a secretary.

"I saw what you did Friday afternoon," she said. "You've got one strong right arm."

Wouldn't Jon be surprised to find his expert coaching had resulted in me slapping Mr. Dawl.

"I don't know you, but I wanted to call," Tina continued. "That slap was also for me and I wish it could have been me doing it. But I saw his grope so if you sue, I'll be a witness." Tina's voice was a breathy rush.

"Let me think about it." But the thought of a lawsuit made me unhappy. Plus our colored paper rendezvous might be considered by some to have been consensual.

"I'll let you know." And we said good-bye.

For the rest of the morning I watched righteous anger build and allowed myself to experience it, then I let it go. And when the anger was gone I saw I could come from a place of calm—and still get what I wanted. I only had to do it once, but it would have to be done right away before he made excuses like the whole thing was my fault and if I hadn't tempted him then none of that ugly business would have occurred. I made the call.

His snooty secretary was surprised to hear from me and used her, "He's in a meeting." I said if I didn't hear from Mr. Dawl in fifteen minutes, the next call he'd get would be from my lawyer. I didn't have one, but he didn't know that.

Twenty minutes later the phone rang. I summoned inner peace and answered.

"What do you want, Ms. Archer? We finished our business."

"You finished yours, but I haven't finished mine," I said, putting a smile in my voice. "There are changes I want made to my severance."

"That's too bad. There's nothing I can do."

"I'm sorry to hear that. I've been harassed and I have witnesses. So I hope this can be settled quickly and within company boundaries."

"That's blackmail!"

"No, it isn't. I always worked hard and when you couldn't get sexual favors, you fired me. You even told me I could stay if I gave in. Well, you were seen and overheard. What I want is reasonable for the abuse," I said in my icy voice.

"And what do you want?" he was calmer than I expected. Maybe he was seeing his bonus stopped, his boat docked, until he could settle our problem.

"I want my severance doubled and my medical insurance paid for the next year."

"I can't do that! I can't make arbitrary changes!"

"We both know that's not true," I responded to his lie. "You determined the severance packages and the home office went along with your decisions."

Caught in his deceit, he was silent. I thought he'd hung up.

"Fine," he finally said. "I'll send you the new forms, but don't let me hear from you again."

"You won't, if everything is in order. And one more thing," something else had occurred to me. "I want a good letter of recommendation too. After all, my work was exemplary. And you know it."

"Okay, whatever. I'm sorry we had to end like this, Diana. We would have made a good team."

With you on top. No thanks.

"So you're going to follow through?"

"Yeah, it'll be in the mail. Anything else?" He was losing steam.

"No. That's it." I heard a click.

"Goodbye to you too," I said, and exhaled. Then a smile crept across my face—then bigger—and bigger—suddenly I stood up and—

"Yes. YES!" I yelled as I danced around my apartment. Success! And from a place of peace. If I'd been angry and attacked him, he would have raised his shields and I would have gotten nothing. This way it was over and I'd restored my self-respect. And he wouldn't to go back on his agreement—the new yacht was sailing.

# Chapter Twenty-One:
# It Might Have Been

*"Whatever you want to be, you will become in the end."*

*Mockingbirds* became my morning alarm. Awakened by their singing in the seagrape tree outside my bedroom window, everyday went right. Initially, I'd considered an exotic vacation, but decided instead to concentrate my recovery in the familiar surroundings of home.

Andrea had passed along a job lead from a friend. I'd interviewed once and a second was planned, but I was in no hurry. I'd been a numb, half-dead drone in my last job and that wasn't going to repeat, ever. My life was not for wasting on someone else's bottom line.

At night I reconditioned my body through sleep. Jon recommended a seminar and I attended.

"Every night your sleep has two phases," the doctor said. "During the first part the body processes food and cleans out toxins in your system. This takes several hours. The break between this phase and the second one is when many people use the bathroom. Next the body repairs and rebuilds itself, especially the immune system. This also takes several hours. When you deprive yourself of sleep, it's the second phase that suffers. Your body never gets to rebuild itself fully. Over time this inability of the body to finish repairing itself can result in more serious illnesses through a weakened immune system."

At first, my rest was plagued by work dreams, but not like ones Edward had. In mine, I was praised for my hard work. But in one, I kicked the boss's butt. At last they faded.

Waking hours were spent rebuilding my body and I became a gym regular. I was still using my workout package and one Wednesday evening, exhausted, after we'd finished...

I grabbed my gear and waved a happy goodbye to my teacher. He was at the snack bar talking with Oscar and BPM, who flexed. I laughed and walked into the parking lot.

Outside it was almost dark and the lights had halos of mist around them. The lot itself was quiet, but there were still late rush-hour cars squishing by on the street. I was thinking I wanted to be bad. I wanted onion rings!

Then I saw a dirty old pickup with no tailgate parked right next to me. Carrying my gym bag as I squeezed between the truck and my car, I thought, why does someone always have to push up beside me? Then I saw the driver stooped down next to the truck's front tire. Startled, I stepped back. He stood up and grinned. I smiled back and seeing the poor condition of his truck, I felt sorry for him. He motioned for me to go ahead so I unlocked the door, tossed in my bag, and started to walk around to the driver's side.

I was interrupted when something hard jammed into the small of my back.

"Not a sound. Get in the truck," said a malevolent muttering voice.

The adrenaline that flooded my system almost caused me to pass out; my knees wavered. He took this for resistance and jabbed me harder.

"You can run or fight, but if you do you're dead," he hissed.

"You can't get away with this!" It was all I could think of to say.

"Maybe not, but you'll be rotting in your grave while I'm rotting in jail. So get in the truck or you'll get it right here." He yanked open the door and shoved me inside.

As he pushed I ripped the worn seat with my knee and then saw the passenger-side door and window handles were gone. I wouldn't be able to jump out or roll down the grimy, cracked glass. But before I could even think of escape, he hit me on the side of my head hard enough to draw blood, but not severely enough to knock me out. "Eyes down! *Bitch*!"

Then uttering a beery curse, he jumped in beside me and used the filthy fingers of his free hand to push stringers of moldy head-liner from his bristly face.

A last quick, hopeful glance upward showed me a nearly full moon was rising. Below, in its reflection on the damp pavement in front of the gym, I saw a woman I knew standing there. I wanted to signal her, but then I saw the gun in his hand and panic crippled me. At least he wouldn't have two of us to hurt.

He started the engine with a grinding roar and acrid exhaust smoke belched upward into the cab from rusted holes in the truck's garbage strewn floor gagging me until I coughed.

"Not used to the finer vee-hickles?" He sneered as we careened into the street. The revolver rubbed me roughly in the ribs. "You crummy bitch! You got it all!" He drove with one hand and made angry, vicious faces at me.

"Everything's always going your way; everything's always so damn pretty. And the rest of us just work and work for nothing. My life ain't worth shit. I hate it!"

He shook the gun in my face where its barrel clipped my nose and scratched my cheek.

"I ain't going nowhere—just work. And you get everything just by smiling and acting hot. It ain't fair. I want pretties, too. And you're going to give them to me."

"I don't have anything to give you." I would have said "sir" if I'd thought it would have helped.

"Oh, you got plenty, baby!" He gave me a lusty look up and down. "Yeah, plenty to give me!" Green spit drooled out of his mouth.

Now...I knew his plan, and a cold paralysis reached my heart.

"Everyone else gets it free so why not me?" He was very angry and had difficulty controlling the truck in traffic. He slowed down. Then, "Don't go getting any ideas about crashing us. You'd be dead before your pretty pink fingers touched the wheel and I'd just dump you on the street and drive off." A sharp prod punctuated his point.

"Not that this piece of junk is much good anymore. And you saw to that you worthless piece of shit!"

"Me?" I squeaked. "Why me?" I prayed his fingers didn't twitch.

"Shudup and I'll tell ya!" Whack!

"Me and my buddy was going home from a wet, crappy day building a rich bastard's waterfront castle. We'd just spent our last few bucks on cool ones when this bitch in front of us slams on her damn brakes and before you can say shit, we smash her ass."

It was me! It was the accident that sent me to the hospital!

"Well, if it ain't bad enough the damn truck's pissin' water, the bitch gets all weepy and goes off in a meat wagon. So what if it's all her damn fault for not seeing us behind her. She cries 'hurt' and off she goes. Everybody loves her! And we get left holding the old shit bag."

"I'm sorry."

"Shudup I told you! Just shudup!" Poke! Poke!

"That ain't half the bad. The cops were mad about the cool ones. Some fell through the floor and busted and the whole thing stank. The ones we was drinkin' filled our pants, but me and my pal, we just looked around like we didn't smell a thing. But the cops, they found our names in that machine in their car so it's off to the slammer. My buddy's still in there! He used my gun to get money and the cops knew about it. Bastards!"

I was now so afraid that I began to shake uncontrollably. He glared at me curiously with a slight smirk on his lips, but continued his rants.

"I stayed in there so long, I got fired! It was shit work and I'm better than that, but I had to have money for rent and cool ones. It's just lucky my kids' old lady got off her fat ass and got a job so now I don't have to pay for them brats to eat.

"And when they finally let me go I find out the landlord guy put all my stuff in the trash. All my stuff! Some was new! I just got it! And here's my new stuff ripped and ruined! Stupid asshole! I was so pissed off I beat the shit out of him and if he's hurting it's *your* fault."

Smack! I tasted blood on my lips.

"Yeah, it's all *your* damn fault. So here I am to see *you*."

I cringed before the blow.

"I bet you wonder how I found you?" his whiskery jaws sputtered.

"That was easy. I went to that cop house all clean and everything and asked for your name and crap so I could give it to my insurance man. Ha!" he laughed, an evil, mucous sound. "I ain't never paid no damn insurance man. But what the hell! I still got all your crap.

"And I been following you ever since and sleeping in my truck. You see how damn nice it is? You see what *you* did?"

It all rushed back. I'd been in such a hurry to get my car I hadn't paid attention to who had hit me. The insurance had covered the repairs and I'd forgotten about the accident in the heat of the office.

"Yeah, bitch. You been lots of places with me, but you just didn't know it. I've sat outside that crappy gym and almost backed over you one night, but that was too easy."

Jab! Jab! My breath wheezed in and out.

"Then I was coming to your place so we could make hot and sexy love, but the truck got stuck in the damn gate. Those bastards that pushed me out just about got themselves knifed.

"Another time I slammed on *my* brakes, but you missed. Then I waited and waited at that coffee dump, but your crummy friend followed you home. I saw you twirling drunk in a parking lot. And that day you went to the beach, my tire blew or I'd have grabbed you then. You have to suffer like I been suffering, bitch. You got to *hurt*!"

I was silent, and felt sick he'd been watching and neither one of us had noticed. If only I'd been a little more observant, I might not be here tonight being hurt by this man. If only... Thick tears leaked from my eyes and dripped on my sweaty shirt.

"Then one time I came inside that gym joint, but they want money and that ain't right. A shit-head in there even hit me! But I creamed him and got the hell out. And I ain't going back. That damn place is real shitty!

"Finally I had enough, and so I was coming to your work and you about crashed the crap out of me again. You're one shitty driver! *Bitch*!

"And you sure do get around, and always with that same ass! He make you all hot and tingly? You're going to get even hotter 'cause I'm the best! Yeah, you're with me now and I ain't waiting no more—you *damn prick tease!*"

As his fury peaked he hit me hard on the shoulder and—the gun fired. Its sound nearly blew my ear apart and its bullet grazed my flesh before it shot through the roof. My head spun and I felt blood run down my neck as I slumped against the seat, a spring scraping my spine.

"Well, shit! Almost gotcha. But not yet bitch. Not yet. I got to do you *first*."

I could hear his words…understand their meaning…I smelled burnt hair…I must still be alive! But as my brain sang with the pain, I knew I was doomed.

As we inched through a knot of traffic the commuters around us, cool in their air conditioning, innocently listened to their radios, talked on their phones, and a few smoked. One truck had a snake's head stuck on the antenna. They were so close yet to reach out would mean instant death.

"Yeah, you'll feel real good with me, Diana, that's for damn sure. Your shitty buddy almost got onto me a couple of times, but I was toooo slick. He's a big loser!" The anger had turned into glee.

"Ha! Ha! Toooo bad! I got his babe now!" Laughing spit sprayed the windshield as the traffic sped up. "His bitch is *mine*! And he'll cry when he finds her *trashed!* Oh yeah!"

I hoped he would; I knew he would.

A couple of minutes passed and then using one hand he jerked the wheel and turned us down a deserted, pot-holed strip of tar that led to a stand of scraggly trees and tall, thick weeds behind a partially-lit parking garage. A short, rutted dirt track led off the pavement and into the small woods. There were junk cars, scattered tires, and assorted garbage heaps. Someone had dumped a refrigerator, thoughtfully removing its door. When he stopped the truck between a wrecked chassis and some forlorn trees, I saw a used condom hanging from one of the skeletal branches.

This was it.

I thought about fighting, but he would only hurt me more. He had all the weapons and I had none. Then as he turned toward me he pulled out a long, wicked knife with a broken tip.

He set the pistol out of reach on the truck's floor, used the blade to cut open my clothes, and then held it to my throat. Pressing me down, he began to explore using his free hand. He had the stench of rancid bacon. I simply lay there as any resistance would have been worse than useless. Finally, with moonlight streaming in through the windshield, I shut my eyes for the last time as my mind detached from my body.

I saw my life as a kettle on a hot stove—boiling and boiling away. When it was scorched dry, it was the end. I saw that through kind deeds I could add water to the kettle and through mistreatment of others I more quickly boiled away the elixir of life. All my activities were nothing but ephemeral steam rising and coiling away from the rapidly bubbling liquid. Beautiful actions added colorful iridescence to the steam, hatred turned it coal black. I was feverish and heart-sick that just as I was coming to my true inner awareness about the wonder, joy, and beauty that were my life itself, it was all going to be snatched away from me by someone in a wasted moment of ignorance, anger, and greed.

Silently some words formed in my mind, "For of all the sad words of tongue or pen, the saddest are these: It might have been!"

"It might have been…it might have…it might…it…" I spoke aloud as my mind drifted away.

Suddenly there was a loud pop and sharp grit showered my face. I opened my eyes a slit. Faster than a striking serpent, a black gloved hand shot through the breaking window. It grabbed my attacker's arm, twisted it away from my neck, and broke his wrist with a snap. The knife dropped to the floor with a clunk. The following painful cry was accompanied by a loud metal scream. As the black-clad fist hammered his face his stinking weight was yanked away, banging and falling to the muddy ground with a gassy smack.

"Please stay calm," said a voice out of sight above and behind me. It sounded like the soothing voice of my teacher. Was I dreaming? Glass chips flew as a shudder of relief rushed through me. I yanked at my cut, bloody clothes.

"Stay where you are and don't move," the voice said hurriedly. And after a second I heard a scuffle. Then silence. Except for distant moans.

Moments later the flashing lights of police cars were reflecting off every un-filthy surface of the truck that had nearly been my tomb.

In the hospital, the police questioned me. They wanted to know who had smashed the window and who had pulled my abductor out of the truck. I was told he had a broken wrist, a crushed nose, a shattered jaw, cracked ribs, and a concussion. And he was demanding a lawyer. He said he'd been set up and that it wasn't his fault. I told the police I hadn't seen my rescuer. Maybe I'd heard a voice, but I might have been delirious.

Andrea retrieved me from the hospital. I had angry bruises on my head and arms, some very sore ribs, and a deep gash on my left temple. Otherwise I was okay, physically.

But at home, in spite of Andrea's attempts to cheer me with homemade soup, crazy stories of boyfriends, and about how my attacker was a mad dog, I sank into despondency. At first I didn't understand and I couldn't believe what had happened. I browbeat myself for being weak while I pushed my chair and ottoman in front of the door. I anguished over my near-death experience and no amount of happiness self-talk could convince me. Reading didn't comfort and I rebuffed all offers of company and sympathy. Flowers from friends made no impression. I even received an arrangement from Mr. Dawl. I kept the bouquet, but threw the note away.

As the days slowly passed I regained my strength. I must have looked like a child curled up with my grandmother's quilt, and later I rooted in closets and looked through plastic bags until…at last…Sunny Bunny! He saw the light of day again! I had temporary comfort as I clutched him.

Gradually I turned to my notes, journals really, where I had meticulously recorded the lessons. When I read them my mind quieted and, to my surprise, I began to operate from a place of inner calm. This led to action. My old life was over—gone. So I decided to clean away the dross, to lift off the dead weight of excess stuff.

I started with my purse. Dumped on the bed, the heap towered and I found enough change to pay for a dinner for two. Then I saw it…bent, twisted, dirty…but the words were still clear. Forgotten, it was the card Stefan had placed in my bag at the restaurant. I had never looked at it and it seemed an eternity ago.

The writing was bold. *"Whatever you want to be, you will become in the end."* I took a lipstick and wrote them on my bathroom mirror.

I *knew* what I wanted to be.

At last, I could think clearly again. Maybe I could leave the safety of my apartment world, and maybe go back to the gym. But between it and me was the scene of the crime and I had to find a way to cross the chasm. If I didn't then that horrible man had won.

In my first attempt I only drove through the parking lot, slowly. But then found I didn't remember where he'd been parked. To me that was good.

The second time I stopped and sat in my car. A memory surfaced—the argument Andrea and I had before our first visit. It made me smile. But this time the quarrel was all in my head and I saw they were only thoughts so I let them go. I would remember to thank her, and soon.

Then I got out and walked to and through the front door.

*I* had won.

When I returned to Four Palms I was a heroine of sorts. More people than I could count came over to congratulate me on my bravery and steadiness in the face of danger. Even people I'd never met. I wondered how so many knew so much. It had to be Andrea. But talking to Irene, I found Andrea must have a new love she hadn't told me about because no one had seen her for a while.

Then my teacher greeted me. He didn't seem surprised. We went into his office and after Jon closed the door he looked at me intently without speaking. Then he pulled me close and hugged me until I thought I would burst. It seemed to last forever. When he finally released me, we sat and while Jon held my hands I told him I appreciated all the kind and comforting messages he'd left. He said, although very concerned, he knew I had to have time to heal before I returned to the world and that if I had wanted or needed companionship it was always there. I nodded and asked him why everyone seemed to know all the details about my incident.

"Okay, I'll tell you." Jon gently squeezed my hands and looked into my eyes.

✳

"As you may recall, I was talking with Jack and Oscar at the snack bar while I waited for my next client to finish his warm-up. I waved and sent peaceful wishes as you walked out and although I've never said anything, occasionally when we've been close I've felt an intense rage and a choking despair. At first I thought it came from you, but soon knew it didn't. That night it was strong. I looked around and even walked outside while you changed, but couldn't find the origin. Now I know, but I wish I'd known sooner.

"Before you left that evening Irene wanted to visit, unfortunately you were out the door before she could catch up. As she watched you cross the parking lot she saw that man duck down. Then Maria, the girl you call HWP, walked past going out front to wait for her boyfriend, so Irene asked her to check on you.

"Maria watched you both get into the truck and as she saw you glance at her from inside she knew something was very wrong. You looked so terrified it scared her. And as you drove away, she made a quick decision and followed—on foot."

"On foot? We drove for miles!"

"Yes, on foot. And for about five miles."

"How?"

"Well, men admire her beautiful legs. They're strong and she's a runner. The miles were no problem except she lost a phone. And she said to tell you she's got a replacement bill for you."

"I'll gladly pay her whatever it costs," I said.

"I think it was a joke. Anyway, while she was frantically running along the sidewalk behind the truck she called Four Palms and spoke to me. We called 911 right away. And then as she told me what she'd seen, I had a sinking feeling because that guy had been around here before. Do you know how Jim got that discoloration on his face?"

"No." I'd seen the bruise the night we'd all gone for coffee, but I'd guessed that maybe Jim had gotten fresh with some woman and she'd slapped him.

"Your assailant came in here that evening without a membership or a pass. When he found out he had to pay to join, he became belligerent and claimed he had the right to free workouts and that he was always being picked on. When asked to leave he punched poor Jim. Then as Jim stepped back from the blow and picked up his glasses, he again asked him to leave. I think the guy got scared when Jim didn't hit him back and he ran his dirty tail right out. He was lucky because Jim's much stronger than he looks and could have beaten him senseless without breaking a sweat.

"I begged Maria to keep following, if she could. But by then the agony had struck and I realized you were helpless, and I felt helpless too. My heart pounded, adrenaline pumped, and sweat poured out so fast it scared not only me, but also Oscar and Jack.

"Then like a whirlwind Jack grabbed his keys and yelled, 'We can't just stand here! We've got to save her!'

"That galvanized us into action! We flew out the door and jumped into Jack's, BPM's I mean, truck and raced after you."

"The three of you? BPM *and* Oscar?" This was getting stranger and stranger.

"Yes. And that's another debt you owe. When Oscar jumped into the truck bed, he crushed Jack's new mountain bike."

"Fine. But tell BPM…Jack, I mean…all he gets is money."

"I will. Then as Jack drove we kept talking to Maria on my phone. We were lucky because Jack, who's now training to be an EMT, had a flashing light and we put it on the truck's cab.

It helped get us through traffic, but in spite of Jack's swerving in and out we couldn't move fast enough for me. I'm glad he ignored my curses."

While Jon talked he'd moved to the edge of his seat, his breath was short, and now his hands tightly gripped mine.

"When we got to where you'd turned off the main road, Maria pointed in the direction of the trees. While running in traffic, she'd thought she'd heard a shot and had already called the police several more times on her other phone.

"We sped around the block and up beside the parking garage, then rushed as fast as we could through the brush and garbage to where he'd parked his truck. We hurried so fast I didn't have time to think.

"As we closed in, Oscar hurried to the driver's door and I ran to the passenger side. Jack was behind me for backup. Your abductor was distracted and didn't hear us coming, but I could feel your terror and his seething rage.

"Then as I looked through the dirty windows, the guy was holding his knife at your throat. And when I saw your sweet lips move and thought I heard you say, 'It might have been,' well...I just lost it. Big time. I smashed the window and broke his wrist. I'd have broken his neck too, if I could have reached it.

"When Oscar saw me strike, he grabbed the locked driver's door and tore it off."

"The metal squeal I heard?"

"Yes. Then as he threw the door aside and the guy dropped the knife, Oscar grabbed his feet and yanked him out. The jerk hit his chest and jaw on the truck's doorsill as he fell and then passed out. I ran around the front of the truck to finish what I'd started, but only got in one hard kick to his head before Oscar held me back. I wanted to beat that bastard to a pulp, or worse, but even I don't argue with Oscar."

"The scuffling I heard."

"Yes."

"Then when Oscar and Jack saw the police coming, they pulled me back into the trees and we stood there until the police were at the truck's doors. Then we got in Jack's truck, picked up Maria, and they *made* me go back to Four Palms to calm down. I guess I really scared them, and me too." He took a couple of breaths.

"Once back at the gym, I frantically called the police and the hospitals until we knew you were all right."

"And that's the whole story." He looked down at our hands.

When Jon finished we sat there in silence. I can honestly say that this was the most amazing story I'd ever heard. I was shocked and surprised, but as the importance of his words sunk in I found it was a good kind of shock, a relieving kind of shock, and I found my terrible experience was finally reaching closure.

"I must apologize," he said at last, his eyes still lowered. "First for my language."

"That's okay," I said. But something else was bothering him. I was safe, so what could it be? It came out in spurts.

"As…I've told you…I've studied, read, and practiced—a lot, but…what if I'd had greater awareness of what my senses were telling me? That man had been in the gym and near me too. What if I hadn't been distracted and had paid closer attention? I might have been able to protect you. All my training wasn't worth much…and then when I saw you in that truck…I just went out of control. I let my Mundane Mind take over and I sprang apart like a cheap watch.

"I want to apologize. What I did…might not have been the best solution. What if it hadn't worked? My emotions and thoughts were so out of control…I wasn't even rational enough to think. I know intellectually that anger and getting even doesn't work, but who knows what would have happened if Oscar hadn't stopped me. That's what I can't seem to get over. *What if…*" And with that he hung his head.

Seeing Jon as he sat there despondent over what he thought he had done wrong aroused such feelings of tenderness and caring inside of me that I slid my chair over next to him and hugged him like he had hugged me. I didn't care who might walk in. I wanted to tell Jon I loved him and that what he had done was right, but my little voice inside said, "He knows how you feel. Just be there when he needs you." We rocked gently together in silence.

To say all of his revelations surprised me would be an understatement. Still, what was so clear to me was that there were people who would take personal risks to help save a near stranger from danger. I would find some way to thank them all.

And there was one final thing I had seen as my teacher was telling the story of my rescue. My attacker had been right. Jon's eyes had filled with tears when he recalled my sad and scared little voice.

# Chapter Twenty-Two: ReBecoming

*"If you stay open to all opportunities
and choose wisely, the miraculous
can happen to you."*

"What do you see when you look at the moon?" I asked early one evening as we reclined on a jetty with gulf waves washing our feet. It had been about three months since my rescue.

"A rabbit," Jon answered. "It's near the left edge facing outward; its long ears slant back from its head and its tail puffs out below them."

"You don't see a man or a scorpion?"

"No, neither of those."

"Why a rabbit?"

"There once was a rabbit who helped lost travelers. Then to save a starving mother and her babies that were in great pain and suffering, he offered to make the ultimate sacrifice. For his kindness and generosity the rabbit's portrait was painted on the moon. Today when we gaze at her face, we see his selflessness shining down on everyone. Do you see how the moon reflects across the water and how her stripe points to us?"

"Yes."

"That's how we're connected to the rabbit. His light glows inside every person and connects us to everyone else."

Then he raised his hand and pointed at the moon. "Do you see what I'm doing?"

"You're reminding me to practice kindness and generosity in my life, and that those qualities are in all of us."

"Yes. Go on."

"I don't know what else."

"I'm telling you to look directly at the teachings and to not let me or anyone else tell you what is true. Go and experience them for yourself.

"Sometimes the moon can be hidden by clouds, but she lets them pass by. The moon doesn't cling and neither should you. So don't grasp the disturbances so often mistaken for life itself, and don't let your happiness be clouded by expectations and dissatisfactions. They arise, drift over you, and pass, leaving your radiance untouched.

"And finally, remember to keep your eyes on the truth and on your path because as you point the moon moves on, and if you don't stay aware you'll soon be pointing to an empty sky."

Lately the pace of his teachings had increased, but that evening the moon stayed silent. The breeze smelled of saltwater and seaweed and fishermen walked behind us.

"Would you like to time travel?" Jon asked later as we finished a snack.

"It's impossible, isn't it?"

"Only in how you perceive it."

"Then how?"

"When you look back over the centuries, which persons are most cherished throughout time?"

"I'll answer for you," Jon continued. "We value those who helped others who were less fortunate, those who were compassionate, and those who taught others to be kind. Their lives and their lessons are immortal. They are the true time travelers.

"Maybe you've read the story by H. G. Wells where a traveler goes to the distant future, over eight hundred thousand years from now, and then returns and reports on his journey. The last line reads, "even when mind and strength had gone, gratitude and a mutual tenderness still lived in the heart of Man." And in the heart of Woman too, I might add."

"That's a powerful message!" I said. "It sounds like what you've taught me."

"Yes, it is. And the sooner we all recognize those truths, the sooner we'll have peace. Even peace on Earth."

"So, Diana," he said, looking at me seriously for a moment. "You've studied hard, regained your internal balance and found your true identity. Your destiny has begun. You're a teacher too, and now like me, you're a conduit for this legacy."

I was surprised by his statement and I didn't feel much like a teacher. "But Jon, how would I even begin?"

"Initially, by being the best example of what you've learned. You won't know who's watching or listening, but as they see your contented life they will want the same. It's hard to cut through worldly distractions, but some will do it. And remember to come from a place of attraction and not promotion because as the saying goes, 'Teachers open the door, but you must enter by yourself.'"

"But I don't know who to teach?"

"Start with your friend Andrea. She seems tired of hurting and soon others will be drawn to you too. When people have suffered sufficiently they will want what you have; they will want you to help them out of the river. And don't forget, you teach what you have to learn. I know that for a fact."

"Yes, but I've got a job offer," I said, "and everything about the company seems right, including the salary. And I can use this opportunity to help me grow instead of have it bury me. So I don't think I'll have time."

"Excellent! You deserve all those good things. But you'll have time to teach, and who knows, maybe some of it will be at work."

I realized I wasn't going to win this debate, so I decided I would go with the attraction principle. If people came to me I'd teach them, but I wouldn't force lessons on anyone, not even Andrea. Those with only a little dust in their eyes would see what I had to offer anyway.

"You mentioned your new salary," he said after a few minutes. "We've never really talked about money, but I'll give you a brief lesson now if you'd like."

"Yes, please." My position was coming with a nice raise, like a reward for all I'd put up with before. But I wondered what kind of lessons Jon would have about finances.

"Here it is," he said. "If you have inner peace and calm, you are satisfied with your life. Being satisfied you don't require and acquire as much, so your outlay is less than your income. Over time the difference builds into a significant amount. This reserve then provides security and a base from which to teach."

"Seems simple. Is that what you did?" I asked.

Jon just smiled. "I work at the gym because I want to help people.

"You also had a good idea about a journal," he continued. "By writing, you remember to stay clear about your intentions and to focus on the path beneath your feet as well as the way ahead. You do this by planning each day to energize your mind and strengthen your body, to review any unskillful choices and decide how to make better ones, and to learn to recognize and appreciate the happiness you already have, and then bring more of it into your life."

"I'd like you to help me."

"For a little while."

A cloud passed in front of the moon. The rabbit was hiding.

"For a little while...?"

"I'll be going away soon," he said. "I've been waiting to tell you because I wanted you to be moving forward in your life again."

"How long will you be gone?"

"I don't know," he said solemnly.

"Oh," was all I could say and now I realized why he was pressing me on the lessons.

The next few weeks quickly passed. Looking back, it appeared to me that ever since my attack, my teacher had not been the same. Maybe I was the one who was not quite the same, but still there was an undertone of unease about him. And I felt a little guilty thinking this change had something to do with me.

I'd finished my training package and we'd begun working out as friends. Exercising together was truly wonderful and I wanted to consummate our relationship, but there didn't seem to be an appropriate opportunity.

Then early one Sunday afternoon Jon called and said he finally knew when he was leaving—soon—the next morning in fact. His plans had just fallen into place.

My heart sank. I knew this was important to him, but he was important to me too.

"Come for dinner," I invited, expecting him to refuse.

"I'd love to," he said.

Then panic hit!

I called Andrea and told her she absolutely had to help me at my place in an hour. I also told her to bring her most seductive things, whatever they might be. She was hesitant, but I told her if they were ruined, I'd buy her new ones.

This aroused her curiosity. Me? Seductive things? Ruined? She was there fast.

First, I asked her to help with cleaning the apartment, washing the sheets and towels. But she quickly claimed seductive culinary expertise, took my wallet, and left for the stores to get groceries and wine. I'd finished and showered before she returned.

"What *took* you so long?" I quizzed and gestured.

"Well, I know you're not working yet so I had to shop and shop to get the best bargains. Besides, Corey, the guy at the wine and cheese store, was so helpful and nice I just had to talk to him and find out all about his life. He promised he'd call."

"Great," I said. "Now please help me with my nails."

She balked at painting my toenails so I did them while she put the food away and the wine in to cool. And then she watched as I applied my make-up. It wasn't quite enough for her, but I didn't recognize myself.

Then I dressed. Andrea's selection of a black teddy and CLMP's had been too risqué. When I'd told her that was a little obvious, and that I'd get a chill during dinner, she'd replied, "What dinner?"

I chose an outfit that was only somewhat suggestive.

She shook her head. "I thought you said you wanted to give him a night to remember?"

"I do, but I'm not throwing myself at him."

"Well, I guess you could stumble on the carpet or something and have him catch you."

I had to smile at my friend.

Then we selected the scent. Andrea wanted me to use the Persuader, but I'd tried that and it hadn't worked. So after sniffing several vials I decided to use a combination, the Persuader and oils from the medieval faire.

"You stink," Andrea said with a bunny wrinkle.

"It'll make up for the outfit."

Then the doorbell rang and we jumped.

"It's him! He's early! Don't let him see you!"

She ran into the bedroom. And came right back out. "You live on the second floor, Diana. I am not going out *that* window."

"Be casual," I told her and opened the door. It was a stranger looking for his date. I told him he was at the wrong place, but from the way he looked at me I knew my outfit was a success.

"That's enough excitement for me," Andrea said. "You're on your own. Some of us have to work tomorrow."

"To success!" And as she held up her empty hand like she was toasting she told me to call her, even at work. I promised I would, but no details.

Jon arrived on time and surprised me.

"Do you bring all your students flowers?" I teased.

"Well...you look lovely tonight." He too was taken by surprise.

"Thank you. Come in." He seemed tired, but his eyes were softly twinkling.

I finished fixing the crab and shrimp casserole and we enjoyed a pleasant meal with talk as light as the lemon soufflé he helped me make for dessert.

"If you want," he said, opening the after dinner conversation, "ask Jim to help you sort out the lessons, that is if you need help.

The sum is greater with the blend of two and as the old English proverb goes, 'a joy that's shared is a joy made double.'"

"I'm not certain what to do, but I'll keep in touch with him. Friends on the path are valuable. And besides, he grows on you." Then biting my lip, I asked, "Can you tell me why you're leaving now?"

Jon was silent for a minute.

"Sure. I've mentioned before that I'd planned to see my teachers, but put off going after meeting you. And Diana, do you remember what I said about wanting to hurt the man that attacked you? Under pressure I didn't come from a place of peace, I came from hatred powered by fear and from ignorance. So I've decided to root out those poisons and I'm going away to work on myself."

I didn't think he needed any fixing, but I wasn't going to argue because I didn't want to spend our last moments together with me interrogating him.

"You'll take care of yourself?" I fought back the tears, but my lip trembled. "And if you have no other reason, do it for me."

"Yes. I'll stay healthy and safe. I plan to return." Jon nervously rustled around. "I guess that's it." He got up and made a move toward the foyer.

"Just a minute. I have something I want to tell you."

I took his hand and eased in close to him. I didn't have the "take me I'm yours" look perfected so this one would have to do. Then as Jon came into my arms I placed my hands on the back of his head and pulled him nearer in a manner that said, "I want more than a friendly hug." When he got to within a few inches, his essence overwhelmed me and my mind went blank.

I closed my eyes and waited for his soft, sweet kiss.

It came…I felt it! On my cheek! My eyes flew open. Jon was in my arms and he'd kissed me on my cheek!

"I know what you want," he whispered. "I've always heard you, Diana, and seen you as you truly are. But it wouldn't be fair after all we have gone through to leave you the way you'd like. I can't ask you to wait, but I value our friendship. And I do care for you. A lot. A lot more than a lot."

We separated, and as Jon opened the door my eyes overflowed. He looked back at me and as I saw my life without him, a sob of loss rose, its pressure unbearable.

Then in one smooth unseen movement his arms were around me. And as I arched backward, my hair hanging down and its clip dropping to the carpet, our chests pressed tightly together and his lips met mine in a kiss—the kiss for which every woman yearns: the one that spreads fire from her lips to her toes; the one that says in a single moment of intimacy everything in a man's heart; the kiss that joins his heart to hers. Forever. And as it ended hours, really minutes, later, I had a vision...of us...so happy...together...

As Jon slowly released me, I said quietly, "The sooner I see you..."

"I know the rest," he said, and disappeared into the night.

Still sparking and woozy the craziest thought went through my mind as the door swung shut on this part of my life. Andrea was going to be so disappointed in me.

For a few days I was fine. Then the old feelings came to see me and tried to claw me into a black hole of despair and bury me. I experienced anguish and upset and for a couple of days it worked. But then I saw they were only storm clouds in my mind and when I stopped clinging, they blew away. I could still miss him, bunches and bunches, but I didn't have to be paralyzed, I could be happy.

I told his picture, "When you return—Watch out!"

✳

One Thursday evening several weeks after Jon's departure we decided to meet for dinner at the old Spanish Main Inn. As Andrea revealed her boyfriend Corey's intimate interests, Stefan's unrestrained laughter helped ease my missing Jon. Then while Andrea ate her dessert, Stefan and I spoke more seriously.

"I certainly was lucky meeting you here that first time," I said, wanting Stefan to know how appreciative I was.

"Yes, it would seem so. But if you only look at chance and luck in the positive sense, you might believe they're random events, like Fortune smiling on you, but that's not really true, Diana. Your happy chance began long ago as you, perhaps unknowingly, readied yourself for its arrival, like a surfer who watches an approaching wave."

"What do you mean?"

"That preparing and deciding must be done before the wave arrives. It's as I told you, your individual choices really do add up. And you made them—mental, physical, and spiritual—to get you there on that blue moon night."

"I did?" I'd forgotten there was a blue moon that evening.

"Yes. And since then," he continued, "you've been patient and had the good judgment to recognize and embrace each new chance: the gym, the trainings, the lessons, and even your visions. You welcomed every opportunity and made it your own. *You* changed your life, not just let life change you.

"Through effort, will, and skillful choices, you altered your fate and remade your destiny. So it wasn't luck at all, it was your own hard work. And now when opportunity beckons you'll choose it with the calm, confidence, inner energy, and timely action necessary for a joyous outcome. Fortune did smile on you that evening, Diana, but only because you had a willing mind."

"Thank you," I said, grateful, and finally happy, meaning satisfied. "I am who I want to be. Happiness is my core and my journey too."

Stefan nodded. "You were already on this course searching in your heart for something more and I'm sure you would have found it, in another time or place perhaps, but found it all the same."

Then he leaned forward, took my hand in his, and said, "Diana, you have sufficient knowledge. You must begin. *Now*." As he said this with a smile into my eyes and a firm handshake I felt something intangible pass between us.

Later, after Andrea had finished her chocolate empanadas in rum sauce and had carefully chosen a grey submarine from the treasure chest, we said our goodbyes.

Late one rainy night before I began my new job, I'd had enough. Even though I had written endless reports and manuals I was having trouble with my journals. Jim had come by to compare notes and I'd enjoyed his company, but writing about myself was difficult. After all, the journals were about me and the reality of my life.

Finally, I picked up my teacher's pen, studied it, and in the space between breaths, I saw it—Bold Traveler! I remembered what Jon had said about time travelers and in a rush it came to me. I would write about my teacher and tell the story of his lessons! But not because I missed him and wanted to please, I would do it because of what Jon had given me. I would make *him* a time traveler. And by making him immortal, I could also help others.

Then as I listened to the thunder drumming outside and within my own heart, the figure from the rock wall stepped into my mind. What had I been told? I had been told to ReBecome. And I was—and I am—and I'm going to! In the timeless flow of each precious day, I wake up, choose anew, and don't go back to sleep. The title was mine and with a flash I let go, soared into the Open Sky, and my story entered our world. Then breathing deeply to quiet the lightning in my mind I saw myself ReBecoming, and rested content in that view.

It was still drizzling later as I gathered up the scribblings of my old life, stuffed them into a trash sack, and headed out to the dumpster. My bare feet wove along the drier lanes of the pavement, but occasionally they splashed in a puddle. I shivered as the damp air gusted about my shoulders and legs, but I glowed inside.

As I approached I swung the bag around and around and then heaved it up and in. As it hit the rim and fell inside, out from the container's dark mouth leapt a soggy, smelly cat, right into my arms. I stumbled backwards with astonishment, but didn't let go.

"Oh, Mr. Cheaters! You've come back! You've come back to me!" Tears mixed with the shower. One leaves and one comes home! I hugged him tightly and our warmth blended. We went home. Together.

Even though you may think happiness is gone forever, if you stay open to all opportunities and choose wisely, the miraculous can happen to you.

I would tell my story to anyone who would listen, keeping no merits from its telling for myself. With gratitude and service I would pass them on to all who needed them.

Jon had said, "When the teacher is ready, the student appears."

And so with my deepest sincerity and appreciation I dedicate this book to you—*my* students.

<u>*ReBecoming*</u>–*the personal process of continuous change facilitated by an individual's desire and belief that they can: 1) Re-aim their intentions, 2) Re-energize their mind, 3) Rebuild their body, 4) Relinquish their unskillful choices, 5) Recognize and Redefine their happiness, and 6) ReBecome.*

*

<u>*The Way of Opportunity*</u>–*the continual practice of making skillful choices with a calm and willing mind which leads to recognizing appropriate opportunities and ultimately to creating an expansive way of life and renewal.*

<u>Blue Moon</u>–1) There are normally three full moons per calendar quarter (three months). Occasionally there is an extra full moon per quarter for a total of four, the third of which is called a 'blue moon.' This occurs every 33 months.

Or: The second of two full moons in a calendar month.

2) A long period of time, i.e. 'once in a blue moon.'

3) In folklore, it's said that when the moon is blue she has a face and communicates with all in her light.

<u>Mundane Mind</u>–the thoughts we have. Through cultural conditioning, the ceaseless wants, aversions, and concepts of the Mundane Mind receive the maximum attention as it thirsts to acquire, attach, and dispose. It's fearful, angry, blames, whines in self-pity and hopelessness, and it plots. "It's as disruptive as a drunken monkey infested with lice."

It can also contain thoughts of happiness that bring relief to our lives, but these thoughts are usually fleeting.

_Open Sky Mind_–the thinker of our thoughts, and sometimes called the 'Self.' It's immense, without beginning or end, a peaceful, joyous spaciousness.

The Open Sky Mind perceives the thought process and knows that thoughts are but a small part of its immensity.

The amount of time we live and fly free in our Open Sky Mind determines the amount of true happiness we experience.

# Open Sky Mind Labyrinth

A labyrinth is an ancient outward symbol for a sacred inner journey. It is both a contemplative and transformational tool. The labyrinth on the following page can be 'walked' with your finger and although conveniently small, is no less challenging than those of full size.

The traditional purpose of the labyrinth journey is to reach the center, finding peace and personal truth there. This version is different. It starts at the center–the Mundane Mind–a place very easy to get to, as shown here by the straight corridor from the everyday world, but a very difficult spot from which to escape. Your challenge is to negotiate the twists and turns in the thought process to successfully reach and stay in your Open Sky Mind. It is only there that perspective is gained and true peace and transformation can occur.

As you slowly trace the spiraling paths with your finger, allow your mind and your knowing heart to flow freely with innate wisdom and reintegrate with your body. This will provide a peaceful intimacy with yourself and allow you to recognize that you are not your thoughts. Repeat as many times as necessary each day and night.

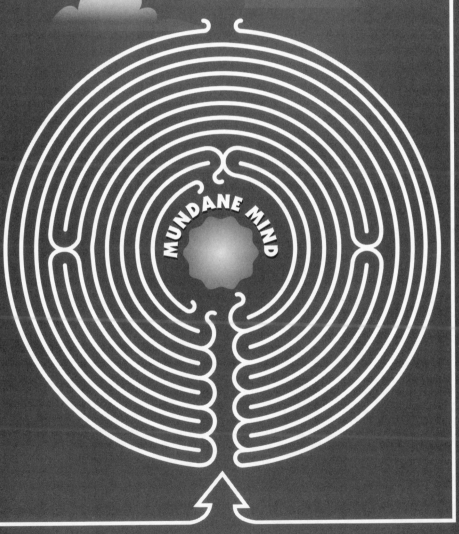

OPEN SKY
MIND

MUNDANE MIND

EVERYDAY WORLD

# Chapter Quotes

Chapter One: "All of life is but a parade of choices."

Chapter Two: "You will grow so far beyond yourself it will be like comparing a shrub to an oak."

Chapter Three: "Pride isn't necessary for a happy life."

Chapter Four: "The joy of life is all around if we could but perceive–and believe."

Chapter Five: "It takes dedication–and a strong back–to be a Bold Traveler in your life."

Chapter Six: "Finding someone who's in the world, but not of it, doesn't happen often."

Chapter Seven: "He'd tell me not to tolerate anything that hurt my self worth."

Chapter Eight: "You will have obstacles and you must pass them, but you will see they are hollow, empty, and you will realize that it is all just appearances."

Chapter Nine: "What's amazing about the secrets of the Universe is...they aren't secret."

Chapter Ten: "The hardest part about going to the gym is going to the gym."

Chapter Eleven: "It was shocking to see I'd worn myself out living up to nothing."

Chapter Twelve: "Extend the quality of equanimity to all. Cool them with the love from within you."

Chapter Thirteen: "We soon find that many of our problems we have caused for ourselves."

Chapter Fourteen: "When we have our thoughts, our lives can be smooth and peaceful, but when our thoughts have us, our lives are full of anger, negativity, and greed."

Chapter Fifteen: "It seems that appreciation and gratitude are always in hindsight."

Chapter Sixteen: "We're experienced, roughened by our lives. We have to prove we're steady swimmers. This is the way of life."

Chapter Seventeen: "My friends, it is neither the wind nor the pole that causes the flag to flap. It is your minds that flap."

Chapter Eighteen: "Don't compare your insides with their outsides."

Chapter Nineteen: "You can't change someone else, but you have control over your own thoughts."

Chapter Twenty: "And when the anger was gone I saw I could come from a place of calm—and still get what I wanted."

Chapter Twenty-one: "Whatever you want to be, you will become in the end."

Chapter Twenty-two: "If you stay open to all opportunities and choose wisely, the miraculous can happen to you."

*Thank You for reading!*
*May you always be filled with joy!*

*And a very blessed Thank You*
*to my teachers, to my family and*
*friends, and to all who enrich my*
*precious parentheses.*